MYTHICAL JOURNEYS, LEGENDARY QUESTS

MYTHICAL JOURNEYS, LEGENDARY QUESTS

THE SPIRITUAL SEARCH – TRADITIONAL STORIES FROM WORLD MYTHOLOGY

MOYRA CALDECOTT

Colour plates by Cheryl Yambrach Rose
Text illustrations by Rachel Caldecott-Thornton

BLANDFORD

First published 1996 in the
United Kingdom by
Blandford
A Cassell Imprint
Wellington House
125 Strand
London WC2R 0BB

Distributed in the United States by Sterling Publishing Co., Inc.
387 Park Avenue South, New York, NY 10016–8810

Distributed in Australia by Capricorn Link (Australia) Pty Ltd
2/13 Carrington Road, Castle Hill, NSW 2154

**A Cataloguing-in-Publication Data entry for this title is
available from the British Library**

ISBN 0 7137 2546 X

Typeset by Litho Link Ltd, Welshpool, Powys, Wales
Printed and bound in Spain by Bookprint

Contents

Preface

A MYTH IS A story almost entirely told in symbol, metaphor and analogy. It is a story which, even without decipherment, works subliminally. At first, and superficially, the myths from thousands of years ago from cultures very different from our own may seem strange and barbaric. Yet, surprisingly, they ring true against our own when once we have decoded their symbolic language.

They have had power to entertain and inform century after century, generation after generation, because they deal with universally important questions. 'Where do we come from?' 'Who are we?' 'Where are we going?' These are questions that are always at the back of our minds, but as yet have never been satisfactorily answered. Myths try to 'access the infinite' in order to answer them and are constructs of the creative imagination.

Legends are somewhat different because they deal more with the progress of the individual soul in this world, and often use the lives of real historical persons to illustrate their point. Over the centuries, with retelling after retelling, the adventures of the protagonist are exaggerated and embellished until at last we can scarcely believe that such a person existed. But if we allow the legend to do its work properly we soon realize that each 'adventure' is an illustration of a universal principle that applies as much to us here and now as to the legendary hero there and then.

Why should we study these ancient stories when there are so many contemporary stories to read? Is it perhaps because every aspect of our lives is complex and mysterious and the more ways we have to help our understanding of them the better? We are so close to our everyday experiences that we often cannot see them for what they are. A new perspective may give a sudden shock of recognition and understanding. The myths and legends of antiquity are still around because, paradoxically, they have proved time and again that they can supply this shock, this 'new' perspective.

One of the most persistent themes in myth and legend is that of the significant journey, no doubt because of our own strong feeling that we ourselves, in our lives, are on a journey. No matter how often literal-minded people and scientists tell us that there is no evidence for this, we cannot shake off the impression that we existed before we were born and will continue to exist after our death.

In AD 627, King Edwin of Northumbria (the Saxon kingdom in the North of England) held a council to discuss whether he and his people should accept the faith of Christ or not, and this was said:

Your Majesty, when we compare the present life of man with that time of which we have no knowledge, it seems to me like the swift flight of a lone sparrow through the banqueting-hall where you sit in the winter months to dine with your thanes and counsellors. Inside there is a comforting fire to warm the room; outside, the wintry storms of snow and rain are raging. This sparrow flies swiftly in through one door of the hall, and out through another. While he is inside, he is safe from the winter storms; but after a few moments of comfort, he vanishes from sight into the darkness whence he came. Similarly, man appears on earth for a little while, but we know nothing of what went before this life, and what follows.[1]

From the great literary masterpieces of Dante's *Divine Comedy* (1307–21), Geoffrey Chaucer's *The Canterbury Tales* (about 1387) and John Bunyan's *Pilgrim's Progress* (1678–84) to those anonymous stories passed down by word of mouth during generations of tribal gatherings, the theme of the journey or the quest has stirred the imagination, stimulated understanding and powerfully charged the will towards renewal and transformation.

In this book I have gathered together only a few of the many stories about the journey, sacred, mythic and legendary, and I have offered in the commentaries only a brief suggestion as to what may be found there. My hope is that readers will be inspired to set off on their own journeys of exploration through the rich and fertile realms of myth and legend.

MOYRA CALDECOTT
Bath, England

1

Gilgamesh: The Quest for Immortality

SUMERIA

Origin

A CYCLE OF epic tales describing the adventures of Gilgamesh originated in Sumeria, the Tigris/Euphrates region of the Middle East, nowadays known as Iraq. The hero was said to have lived in Uruk not long before or after 3000 BC, at the height of the Sumerian civilization. Gilgamesh was described as the king of Uruk, one of the major cities of the region, others being Ur and Kish. Early tablets record his battle with King Agga of Kish suggesting that in fact Gilgamesh was a historical figure. Later tablets exaggerate his prowess and ascribe feats to him that could only have been performed by a mythic hero with some divine blood in his veins. It came to be said that he was the son of a human father, King Lugalbanda of Uruk, and the goddess Ninsun.

A SUMERIAN

The earliest records of his life are in Sumerian, but later the Semite peoples who overran the region took the story up and most of our information comes from clay tablets in the cuneiform writing of the Akkadian language. Babylonian fragments are older than the Assyrian, and trading links with the Hittites (from what is now modern Turkey) and the Hurrians (from what is now modern Armenia) later carried the epic even further afield. Fragments have been found by archaeologists in the archives of Boghazkoy, the ancient Hittite city, and at Megido, but most of what we have today were found in the ruins of the great library of Nineveh, which was sacked *c.* 612 BC. The ancient Elamites were known to have performed a version of it as a drama. There is currently an English dramatic version in existence written by Robert Temple, author of an excellent verse translation of the epic called: *He Who Saw Everything*.

CHERYL
YAMBRACH
ROSE ©

The Story

GILGAMESH, THE GREAT king of Uruk, and his inseparable companion, Enkidu, returned in triumph from the conquest of the giant guardian of the cedar forests, Humbaba. The goddess of love, Ishtar, seeing the young man riding in the streets, his muscles rippling and his curls bound with gold, desired him and called him to her presence.

Gilgamesh stood before her proudly – aware of the scent of a thousand flowers, dazzled by the gleam of her skin and the jewels that twined in long strings around her limbs.

'Gilgamesh,' she said softly, 'come closer. I offer you the greatest treasure any man could desire.'

'What is that, my lady?' the hero asked cautiously, keeping his distance.

She smiled fondly and reached out her slender hand, each finger circled with a different gem.

'You will be my lover,' she purred. 'Come closer, mortal, and taste a greater pleasure than you have ever known.'

Still Gilgamesh held back.

'Come!' she repeated, this time a trifle impatiently.

'Great goddess,' he said, 'I am a king and already have all the treasure any man could desire.'

Her eyes narrowed.

'Forgive me, goddess, but all who have been your lovers are no more. To lie with you is to lie with death.'

'Go then, Gilgamesh, and taste the venom of my curse!' Her eyes flashed. Her lips tightened. Her voluptuous body seemed to harden and grow tall and angular. She towered over him and the sky darkened behind her.

He retreated.

Then Ishtar went to her father, Anu, god of the firmament, and demanded that he avenge the insult that Gilgamesh had given her. Her father at first refused and protested that Gilgamesh was a great hero and had much still to do for the gods.

But Ishtar grew shrill in her demands and declared she would open the seven gates that were between the upper and lower world so that the dead would escape and harass the living.

'Give me the Bull of Heaven, father, to trample down his kingdom or the dead will outnumber the living on your earth!'

Anu sighed, and gave her the Bull of Heaven.

Triumphantly, she released him in Uruk, the city of Gilgamesh.

He roared and rampaged through the streets, but Gilgamesh heard him and he and Enkidu came out to meet him.

'What sport, friend!' Gilgamesh cried with shining eyes.

'What sport, indeed!' Enkidu replied, and together they wrestled the mighty Bull of Heaven and brought him to the ground. Then, with his bare hands, Gilgamesh ripped him apart and sacrificed his heart to Shamash, the sun god. He mounted the horns on the walls of his bedchamber, laughing at Ishtar's puny attempt at revenge.

To his people he boasted:

> Who is the most splendid among heroes?
> Who is the most glorious among men?
> Gilgamesh is the most splendid among heroes!
> Gilgamesh is the most glorious among men![1]

Ishtar went to the Assembly of Gods in a rage and persuaded them at last that Gilgamesh and Enkidu had overstepped the bounds of human arrogance once too often.

'One of them must die,' they agreed, 'and the other must suffer at his death.'

One night Enkidu dreamed that he would die.

'As I was standing there between the heaven and the earth,' Enkidu told Gilgamesh, 'I saw a young man whose face was dark . . .' He shuddered. 'He transformed me with his magic into his double . . . and I found my arms were wings like a bird.'

Gilgamesh tried to comfort his friend, but he would not be comforted.

From this time on, day by day Enkidu became weaker and weaker until he was so ill that he could not rise from his bed. In spite of the power he had as king over a mighty nation, Gilgamesh could do nothing to save his life.

Enkidu died.

Gilgamesh wept.

> What is this sleep that has now come over you?
> You have gone dark and cannot hear me![2]

For seven days he watched beside Enkidu's bed, unable to grasp that he was not coming back. That he was *never* coming back!

At last he gave up hope and moved away in despair.

He left his palace, he left his city, and he wandered in the wilderness living like a beast, uprooting tubers and reaching for berries. He tore off his fine clothes and wore the skins of animals. Not only was he desolate at the loss of his companion, but he was deeply shocked at the power of death. He realized that he, too, would lie so cold and dark one day, and would no longer have access to the bright splendours of the world. He railed against the gods that put this terrible doom on man and determined that he would find a way of living for ever. The riches he had as king were worthless if he could not have eternal life.

He remembered a story about a man called Ziusudra who, in the ancient days, had survived a flood that had destroyed the rest of mankind and had been given the gift of immortality by the gods. He determined to seek him out.

For a long time he journeyed across the wilderness of the world until he came at last to the mighty mountains of Mashu, through which he must pass if he wanted to reach the Underworld. His way was barred by the fearsome guardians of the mountains, half giant scorpion and half man and woman.

'No man has ever crossed through these mountains and lived,' said the scorpion-creature, raising his sting.

But Gilgamesh stood firm. He told of his heroic deeds and of his sorrow and despair.

'If you can face the darkness of the mountain,' the guardian said, 'it will be Shamash, the sun god himself, who will decide your fate on the other side.'

The scorpion-creature rolled back the gate to the mountain, and the rocks rumbled and groaned beneath it.

Gilgamesh journeyed into the darkness of the mountain, travelling along the path the sun takes when it does not shine upon the earth.

Hour after hour he walked in darkness denser than he had ever experienced before. Hour after hour his spirits sank lower, his despair weighed heavier. And then, after the ninth hour, he felt a slight breeze and his step quickened. After the twelfth hour, he walked out into the brightness of the sunrise on the other side of the mountain.

He found himself in a garden of jewels. Leaves, flowers and fruit gleaming in the early sunlight were all made of the most precious gems. He gazed about in wonderment, almost forgetting his quest.

But remembering at last, he journeyed on.

After a time, he came to a tavern where the tavern-keeper was a woman-being called Siduri whose task it was to dispense calming and hallucinogenic drinks to those on the way

'SCORPION-CREATURE'

to the Underworld. Gilgamesh looked so wild and desperate, and his clothes were so ragged and filthy, that she at first barred her door against him.

He beat on the door, announcing his name and a list of all the great deeds he had done.

'If you are Gilgamesh, the great king of Uruk,' she said doubtfully, 'why are your cheeks so wasted, your face so sunken? You have the look of one who has come from afar.'

He told her of how Enkidu had died and how he had since wandered the wilderness, living like a beast. He told her who he was going to meet, and why.

She opened her door to him.

'The way from here lies over the Waters of Death,' she said. 'No man can cross them and return alive. Why do you waste your time worrying about death? Make merry by day and night while you live. Each day should be a feast of rejoicing. Let your garments be sparkling and fresh, your head washed, your body bathed in sweet scents. Enjoy the little one that holds your hand, and the wife who lies in your bed.'

But he would not listen to her and persuaded her to allow him to try to cross the great sheet of water that lay between the worlds – the Waters of Death.

She told him the only way he might be able to do it would be with the help of the boatman, Urshanabi, who had ferried Ziusudra across all those centuries before.

On her advice he sought Urshanabi in the forests, the flash of the boatman's axe attracting his attention.

Again he was questioned.

'Why have you been wandering the wilderness like one pursuing a puff of wind?'

Urshanabi listened to the great feats Enkidu and Gilgamesh had performed, and nodded his head when Gilgamesh told him of his despair at the death of Enkidu.

'I believe that Ziusudra, the one man granted immortality by the gods, will be able to help me,' Gilgamesh said, 'and Siduri told me that you are the man who can take me to Ziusudra.'

Urshanabi pondered the problem.

'Go to the forest,' he said. 'Cut and shape 120 punt-poles. When you have done this, bring them to where my boat is moored.'

Gilgamesh wielded his axe and cut and shaped 120 punt-poles, and together they embarked upon the Waters of Death. Urshanabi warned Gilgamesh that he must not at any time allow any part of himself to touch the Waters.

'As each punt-pole is consumed, you must throw it away and bring out a fresh one.'

The punt-poles were used up before they reached the other side, but Gilgamesh took off his loincloth and made a sail of it to continue his journey.

Ziusudra, who lived at the meeting of three rivers, looked out across the Waters of Death and saw the boat with its strange sail. He wondered that it seemed not to have its usual master at the helm.

When Gilgamesh disembarked he lost no time in telling Ziusudra his story and how he longed for eternal life. Ziusudra, like all who had met Gilgamesh before on this journey, warned him that mankind is no more than a fragile reed and cannot expect permanence. Nothing is permanent on earth:

> The dragon-fly emerges and flies.
> But its face is in the sun for but a day.[3]

'If this is so,' Gilgamesh asked Ziusudra, 'how is it that you, a man like myself, have entered the Assembly of Gods and found everlasting life?'

Ziusudra told him about the great Flood in ancient times that destroyed all the rest of mankind. He was warned to build a boat and take on board 'the seed of all living creatures'. He built it in seven days, on instruction, as a cube and sealed it against the storm that was to rage for six days and seven nights.

At sunrise on the seventh day after the storm arose, he looked out and found that it had abated. All had gone deadly quiet.

'All men had returned to clay,'[4] said Ziusudra.

The boat eventually came to rest on the peak of Mount Nisir.

When seven days had passed and it seemed to him that the waters were receding, he sent out a dove. Finding no trees on which to rest, it returned. After another seven days he sent out a swallow. The swallow also returned. But when, in another seven days, he sent out a raven, the raven did not return. Ziusudra offered sacrifices and oblations on the mountain-top in gratitude for his survival.

But the Assembly of Gods was in an uproar. It seemed that Enlil, who had ordered the storm because of his anger at the human race, was furious that any living creature had survived, while the other gods were shocked at the extent of the devastation. Ishtar, in particular, wept for her people, and Enki spoke passionately about the injustice of punishing all for the sins of a few.

Enlil began to regret what he had done and agreed that Ziusudra, a human, should be given eternal life in recompense for what his race had suffered.

Gilgamesh listened carefully to the story of how Ziusudra became immortal. If one mortal could become immortal, he thought, surely it would be possible for another – especially one such as he? He would be the first mortal to become immortal by sheer will-power. Ziusudra laughed.

'You cannot even ward off sleep for six days and seven nights,' he told Gilgamesh. 'How then can you expect to ward off death?'

Gilgamesh boasted at once that of course he could ward off sleep for six days and seven nights, and prepared to demonstrate it.

Ziusudra's wife baked cakes, and each night Ziusudra placed one beside the bed of Gilgamesh to give him refreshment in the night. But each morning the cake was uneaten because Gilgamesh had slept.

Gilgamesh was forced to admit defeat and Urshanabi was instructed to take him back the way he had come. Ziusudra provided the king with fresh, clean clothes, and he washed himself before he set off.

As they parted, Ziusudra was moved to give him a gift. He told him one of the secrets of the gods. It seemed there was a flower that bestowed immortality – but it grew at the bottom of the sea where no man could reach it.

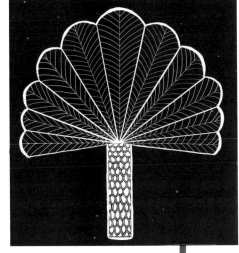

Nothing daunted, Gilgamesh tied stones to his feet and sank beneath the surface. He found the plant, plucked it and brought it back.

'I will take it to my people,' he cried triumphantly, 'and we will live for ever!'

Ziusudra watched him go, wondering if indeed he would achieve immortality.

Long, long was the journey back with as many dangers as there had been on the way out.

Gilgamesh carried the plant carefully and after twenty leagues broke off a morsel. After

TRADITIONAL DESIGN FROM
STONE RELIEF CARVING

thirty more he rested beside a pool. As he refreshed himself in the water, a snake slithered out from behind a rock, smelling the scent of the flower. Quick as lightning, it seized the plant and swallowed it. Horrified, Gilgamesh was in time to see it slough its skin and be rejuvenated before it slid from his sight.

For a while he sat beside the pool bewailing his fate. There was now nothing to be done but return home empty-handed. Wearily, he travelled the last miles to Uruk and then, on a hill overlooking the city, he paused. What he saw was a goodly place with great ziggurats and palaces and temples; with gardens and broad streets where happy people walked up and down; where children laughed, and lovers kissed.

He straightened his shoulders and strode down to reclaim his kingdom.

Commentary

GILGAMESH, WITH HIS mixed blood, had something of a primitive god's restless ambition for glory combined with the frustrations of being mortal and having only limited time in which to achieve what he desired.

The story goes that when Gilgamesh succeeded his mortal father as king of Uruk, he was thoroughly disliked and feared by his subjects. The young man was an arrogant despot, continually interfering in their lives. In exasperation, they pleaded with the goddess Arura to give him a fitting companion who would somehow occupy his time and draw away some of his attention from his subjects. She agreed, and chose Enkidu, a wild man living among the animals of the mountains and forests. It was said that he could communicate with the natural kingdom and was much hated by hunters because he released their prey from traps and warned the animals of the approach of danger. To prepare him for the great change that was about to take place in his life a harlot was employed to seduce him. She bathed and scented him, and for six days and seven nights he lay with her until he was weak and satiated. When she left he found the animals shunned him, for he now had a human smell.

At their first meeting Gilgamesh and Enkidu fought, rather like the heroes Little John and Robin Hood in the British cycle of myths. After this trial of strength the two became firm friends with deep respect for each other. There are many tales from Mesopotamia of their extraordinary feats of strength, not least among them their defeat of the giant guardian of the cedar forests, Humbaba (Huwawa).

The death of Enkidu after the rejection and mocking of the goddess Ishtar took Gilgamesh from the heights of his arrogance to the depths of despair as he realized the fact of his own mortality. These events happened approximately 5000 years ago and yet we still respond to them, knowing that they are the events, albeit metamorphosed by symbolism, of our own lives. The cry of Gilgamesh beside his dead friend is our own cry as we look at someone close to us lying dead.

> What is this sleep that has now come over you?
> You have gone dark and cannot hear me!

That Gilgamesh, the warrior, had gone so far in life without realizing the full implication of death is not as surprising as it seems. Until it touches those close to us, we too do not fully register the implications of death. When we do, we also set off on an inner journey of enquiry – disturbed by questions we cannot answer.

We, like Gilgamesh, have to face the mountains of Mashu – the impediment to true understanding thrown up by all the false but comforting propaganda we have been fed throughout our lives. The guardians of the mountains are scorpions, for truth has a sting in its tail and it is truth we seek. If we can convince them that we are earnest in our quest, they will let us pass.

The twelve hours of the night in the dense darkness of the mountain remind us of the 'dark night of the soul' the great Christian mystics speak about – the darkness we have to pass through when we leave all the comfortable misconceptions of our former lives and set out in search of true illumination. We nearly despair, until we feel the faint breeze of dawn at last, which is the first indication we have that our spirit is stirring to the rising of the sun (the source of light).

As we emerge from the darkness of our doubt and our despair, our first reaction is tremendous relief and joy. The world seems a garden of jewels – precious, wonderful, dazzling. We see everything we had seen before in a new light and appreciate everything much more than we had before. We are in this euphoric state of relief after that rigorous journey through the mountain and forget, for the moment, that we have not yet arrived at our true destination – and that flowers are *not* jewels.

When we are ready to leave the garden and travel on we come to the tavern of Siduri, where we may still be lulled into a sense of false euphoria. We are tired of the struggle. It would be so pleasant to relax and accept her advice that we should 'eat, drink and be merry'.

These early texts of the epic of Gilgamesh were known throughout the Middle East at the time the Hebrew biblical texts were being compiled, so it is interesting to compare Siduri's words with those in Ecclesiastes 9.7–9, as J. B. Pritchard has pointed out:[5]

Ecclesiastes

Go thy way, eat thy bread with joy, and drink thy wine with a merry heart; for God hath now accepted thy works.

Let thy garments be always white; and let thy head lack no ointment.

Live joyfully with the wife whom thou lovest all the days of thy life of thy vanity, which he hath given thee under the sun [. . .] for that is thy portion in this life, and in thy labour which thou takest under the sun.

Siduri

Make thou merry by day and night,

Of each day make thou a feast of rejoicing,

Day and night dance thou and play.

Let thy garments be sparkling and fresh,

Thy head be washed, bathe thou in water.

Pay heed to the little one that holds thy hand.

Let thy spouse delight in thy bosom,

For this is the task of mankind.

We are tempted but, if we are determined enough to pursue our journey, we move on. Surely life is more than this? But can it be more with death waiting to cut it short at any moment? Gilgamesh meets Urshanabi, the boatman (reminiscent of the boatman, Charon, who ferries the dead across the Waters of Death in Greek mythology). So many myths have the concept of life originating from the deep primeval 'waters', which existed somehow before existence itself was conceived by the Creator, that it seems logical there should be a return to the primeval waters – or at least a passage over them – at death.

In a sense we have to think about the beginnings of life, the very basis of existence, in order to make sense of death. We have to contemplate the ultimate origin from which duality, and all that followed from it, sprang. But we are not ready to plunge into the depths yet – it is not our time to die – and we may only skim over the surface at this point. Each prop (each punt-pole) we use will be taken from us until we have none left. This is the most dangerous time of all. Many lose their sanity at this point, faced by the loneliness and vastness of the primeval waters. But Gilgamesh, the true hero, improvises a sail to continue forward. We cannot know what this sail will be, in our case, until every support we have relied on has gone. But we must remove every vestige of 'clothing' we have brought from the past and enter this new phase as basic and naked as we were born; without preconceptions, without advice or support from family and friends.

We come to Ziusudra, the man who survived the wrath of God. His story encourages us to believe that it *may* be possible to survive death. The story of the Flood in the Gilgamesh epic is extraordinarily like the story of Noah in the Bible. Why was this story found so important by the Jews that it is retold in the Bible? Perhaps the story of such a flood is a warning to us that we are always on the edge of extinction. We exist only by the grace of God and if He withdraws His grace we are extinguished.

When I read the description of the storm that brought about the flood in the epic of Gilgamesh I remembered a description of a storm from the same region by A. H. Layard, the excavator of Nineveh and Babylon.

> On the sixth of April we witnessed a remarkable electrical phenomenon. During the day heavy clouds had been hanging on the horizon, foreboding one of those furious storms which at this time of the year occasionally visit the Desert. Late in the afternoon these clouds had gathered into one vast circle, which moved slowly round like an enormous wheel, presenting one of the most extraordinary and awful appearances I ever saw. From its sides, leaped, without ceasing, forked flames of lightning. Clouds springing up from all sides of the heavens, were dragged hurriedly into the vortex, which advanced gradually towards us, and threatened soon to break over our encampment.[6]

Ziusudra makes Gilgamesh perform a practical experiment to drive home to him the impossibility of avoiding death by will power. He asks him to try to do without sleep for six days and seven nights. He cannot, and has at last to admit defeat.

Pity for his fellow human (or is it a further test?) prompts Ziusudra to tell Gilgamesh the secret of the flower that renews youth. Gilgamesh plunges to the bottom of the sea – the ocean of divine consciousness into which we may only be aware of venturing when we are in the highest state of our own spiritual consciousness. Gilgamesh has come so far, discarded so much and learned so much, that he is now capable of achieving the flower. But is he capable of keeping it? Evidently not. The snake, the serpent ever present in Eden, plays his natural role. The chthonic forces of the Underworld, or our subconscious, do not allow us to become gods. We are human and fail every time in the final test. How often do we experience briefly a potent and important truth, only to lose it again as we fall back into, and are swamped by, the trivia of daily life?

But had Gilgamesh ultimately failed? When Gilgamesh saw his city again he saw it as a goodly place. He had come to accept life on its own terms – not in the sense of carefree and careless abandonment of all responsibilities and principles implied in the advice to 'eat, drink and be merry', but in the sense of appreciating what he had. He no longer saw a garden of jewels but instead a city of stone and mortar, with gardens of real flowers and people who were mortal, but were going about their business with enjoyment. Before Gilgamesh set off for home he washed and changed his clothes. The return journey is a different journey. It is not just a matter of retracing his steps. The despair and grief is no more. He is a new man.

The Babylonian name Gilgamesh means 'He Who Saw Everything'. This is the title that Robert Temple chose for his verse translation of the epic. This gives us a clue that Gilgamesh, as long ago as Babylonian times, was no longer looked on as a purely historical figure but, like the British King Arthur, had passed into the potent realm of myth and legend where he teaches us through the magic of metaphor, symbol and archetype what we need to know about ourselves.

However, we must not forget that these ancient myths are as much about the natural phenomena of the world as they are about the development of the human soul. Tammuz, the lover of Ishtar, is ritually slain and has to spend half the year in the Underworld like Persephone in the Greek myth, indicating the change of seasons. Robert Temple develops a very interesting interpretation of the myth of Gilgamesh using astronomical and astrological references. The Flood itself occurs so often in myth because it is a natural phenomenon that periodically devastates great tracts of land and destroys homes and peoples. The 'Wilderness' of Enkidu and his closeness to the animal kingdom followed by his subsequent divorce from it, are suggestive of our own evolution – our closeness in palaeolithic times to the animal kingdom, and our subsequent break from it as we build houses and communities and civilizations.

Gilgamesh is a most human hero. He is boastful, arrogant, thoughtless, courageous, charismatic. But he suffers and learns, and he changes. We are with him through all his vicissitudes. He longed for immortality and 5000 years after his life and death we are still talking about him!

THE WATER GOD

2

Jason and the Quest for the Golden Fleece

GREECE

Origin

THIS LEGEND WAS already an old and well-known tale in Greece when Homer came to write the story of the Trojan War in the ninth century BC, for he refers to it on several occasions as though his audience would already be familiar with it. Much later, Euripedes, Aeschylus and Sophocles used the material in drama. Perhaps the best-preserved and most complete version we have today was written in the third century BC by the scholar Appolonius Rhodius, once the pupil of Callimachus, tutor to the Ptolemies of Egypt and chief librarian of the magnificent library at Alexandria, which contained the most authoritative ancient texts in the world before it was burned down by the Romans.

A GREEK SHIP

The Story

WHEN HIS FATHER, King Aeson of Iolcos, was ousted from the throne by his half-brother, Pelias the Terrible, the infant Jason was taken secretly from the palace and carried to the Mountain of Pelion where he was left to be reared in safety by the centaur Chiron. There he spent a happy youth unaware that he was heir to the throne of the rich and fertile land he saw far below him on the plain.

Chiron, half man and half horse, now venerable with age and wisdom, was tutor to a great many sons of heroes and kings. His pupils learned all the skills of peace and war – strength and agility of body and mind; knowing when to rely solely on self or when to work with others; the importance of honour in all dealings, whether it be in consideration for others in small things or in the keeping of one's word in the face of death. The boys worked and played on the steep and rugged slopes of the mountain and slept at night deep in Chiron's cave. Not a day passed but Chiron drew out his golden harp and sang to his charges the stories that had come down to him from his ancestors. These stories held their attention not only for the adventures they described and the beauty of the words and sounds he used, but also because they contained

A LYRE

layer upon layer of meaning. So, in a very pleasant way, their understanding of themselves and the world around them was enriched.

When Jason was grown almost to manhood he questioned Chiron so earnestly about his parentage that the aged centaur decided it was time for him to reveal it. When Jason heard how his uncle Pelias had seized the throne from his father he determined to return to Iolcos and restore it to its rightful owner. Chiron watched the youth set off, hoping that he would not forget anything of his training on the mountain, for now was the time it would be put most severely to the test.

In the valley at the foot of the mountain flowed a river, so swollen with melting snow that it was a raging torrent. While Jason gazed at it in some alarm, wondering how he was to get over it, he felt a tug at his arm and found a frail old crone at his elbow begging him to carry her over to the other side. He tried to tell her it was not possible, but she was so agitated and so insistent that at last he put her on his back and waded into the torrent. Many times he stumbled on the rolling pebbles and many times he was almost swept away. At last he managed to reach the further bank and lay gasping for breath on a smooth rock. When he had sufficiently recovered he looked around to see how the old woman was faring. To his astonishment, he saw a tall and regal young woman standing in a sphere of light so blinding that he raised his hand to shade his eyes.

She smiled at him, discarding the last vestige of the old crone's rags.

'I am Hera, Queen of Heaven,' she said. 'You have helped me and I shall not forget it, Jason of Iolcos.' And then she was gone like the sparkle on water when a shadow falls upon it.

He rubbed his eyes and stared about him, but there was no sign of anyone present but himself. Bemused, he set off towards the city he had seen from the mountain-top. He noticed that one of his sandals had been lost in the river.

As he came to the outskirts of the town he was surprised at how curiously people looked at him. In particular, they pointed at his one sandal and whispered among themselves. He could not know that Pelias, the king, had been told by a soothsayer that his kingdom would be wrested from him by a stranger with only one sandal.

His spies spotted Jason, so the cunning Pelias sent out courtiers to greet him and invite him as a guest to the palace, hoping to render him harmless by the rules of honour governing host and guest. Jason was feasted and entertained royally, and during the entertainment was told the story of the Golden Fleece. It seemed that a certain King Athamas of Boeotia had two children, Phrixos and Helle. When he married again their cruel stepmother devised a way of getting rid of the eldest son. She boiled the seed before sowing so that it would not germinate, and then bribed messengers from the Oracle of Delphi to say that the only way Athamas would be able to feed his people would be if he sacrificed his first-born. Sadly, Athamas was about to do this when a golden ram appeared and called out in human voice to the lad, instructing him to climb upon its back. While all were standing astonished, Phrixos managed to dodge the knife and leap on to the back of the beast. His sister Helle climbed up behind him and the ram took off like Pegasus and flew away towards the east. Over islands and oceans it flew. At one point Helle lost her grip on its fleece and fell to her death. Later, that place was named the Hellespont after her. Phrixos clung on and was deposited at last safely on the shores of a distant land, Colchis, at the furthest end of the stormy Euxine Sea. There, on the ram's own instructions, he sacrificed it to the gods who had saved his life, and hung its golden fleece on a sacred oak tree deep in the forest.

King Aietes of Colchis took the young lad into his court, and he married one of the king's daughters, Chalciope, who bore him several sons. As time passed King Aietes became more and more sure that the fleece that had come into his kingdom so miraculously was meant for him to keep, and he placed a huge serpent at the base of the tree to guard it against robbers.

Phrixos died in Colchis, but his spirit longed for his home country and would not rest until the magical fleece had been returned there. Over the years, many had tried to fetch it back, Pelias said, but all had met with death long before they reached the land of Colchis.

Jason listened to the story fascinated, while Pelias wove his web.

'If a kinsman came to your kingdom,' he asked Jason at the end of the feasting, 'and was intending to kill you and take your kingdom from you, what would you do?'

Jason laughed. 'I would send him in search of the Golden Fleece,' he said. 'Thus I would not have his blood on my hands, yet that would be the last I'd see of him.'

Pelias smiled.

'You have chosen your own fate,' he said. 'Your blood will not be on my hands, but you will not take my kingdom by force. If you bring me the Golden Fleece my kingdom will be yours. I swear it.'

Jason, who had drunk much wine that night, sobered up and saw the trap in which he had been caught. No matter. He would win the Golden Fleece and regain his father's kingdom without shedding family blood.

Jason then sent out a herald throughout Greece to call for the strongest and ablest heroes to accompany him on this dangerous quest. While he waited for their arrival, Argus, the greatest shipbuilder in all Greece, made the ship they would row and sail to Colchis. It would have place for fifty oars, one for each hero. He tarred the wood with black pitch to make it waterproof, and painted the bows vermilion. Jason named the ship the Argo, after its creator, and gave the shipwright himself an honoured place among the crew.

Fifty heroes were chosen, many of whom had been Jason's companions on Mount Pelion under the tutorage of the centaur Chiron. The gigantic Hercules, engaged on the fourth of his twelve labours, made short work of wrestling the Erymanthian boar, in order to join the crew of the Argo. With him he brought his young squire, Hylas, the most beautiful of boys.

Jason at once asked him to captain the ship, but he refused, saying that no one was worthy to lead them but Jason himself. Tiphys was chosen as steersman because of the skill he had shown on other voyages. Others were Butes, the fairest of men; Castor and Polydeuces, the twins born to Leda and the swan; Caeneus, so strong not even a pine-trunk could fell him; Zetes and Calais, the sons of Boreas, the north wind, and the human Oreithyia. It was known that they could fly, if necessary. Another hero was Peleus, the father of Achilles who, much later, distinguished himself in the Trojan War. Telamon and Oileus also had young sons who later fought in the Trojan War. Mopsus, who could converse with birds, did not have the strength of the others but was a soothsayer of no mean repute. Then there was Idmon, the prophet, and Ancaios, the astrologer, and many more. When they were nearly all gathered and the ship had taken shape, Jason sought out Orpheus in Thrace. He had been one of Jason's companions in Chiron's school for heroes. Orpheus, weary of wandering, was at first reluctant to come, but at last agreed, taking Jason to Dodona where the great oak oracle stood. They cut a bough from the tree and nailed it to the ship.

When the time came to launch the ship they found it was too heavy to move. They consulted the bough from Dodona and were told that Orpheus must play his harp and sing. This he did, and at the sound of his beautiful and melodious voice, the ship began to slide forward. From the Argonauts and the crowds gathered on the beaches nearby, a great shout of joy went up.

As a last act before they set off they slew a bull and offered it as a sacrifice to Hera, the goddess who had promised to remember Jason's kindness to her in the matter of the flooded river. Orpheus held up a golden goblet containing bull's blood, wheat flour, honey, wine and seawater and bade them drink, vowing as they did so to be loyal unto death to Jason and his quest. They set off at last, the plume of smoke from the sacrificial pyre indicating that the winds were right for the beginning of their journey.

Their first landfall was at the base of Mount Pelion, and there the heroes disembarked to visit their beloved tutor Chiron one last time before they sailed away into the dangerous unknown. They found him listening to the boy Achilles playing a harp, but he broke off at once, delighted to see them again. That night he sang to them of the great battle the centaurs and their enemies, the Lapiths, had fought in years gone by. The centaurs had lost because they let wine cloud their judgement. Then Orpheus sang of the first chaos before the world was made, and the fact that all things sprang from Love who could not live alone in the Abyss. The trees, the rocks and all created things listened to his song. The heroes sat quiet. His words, like seeds, took root deep in their hearts.

At dawn they returned to their ship and picked up the oars. They rowed past Mount Olympus where the gods lived in the cloud above the summit, protected by mighty cliffs of rock. They cast many an anxious glance at that forbidding place – but passed it in the end without incident.

They rowed and rowed across the open sea until at last they came to the island of Lemnos. There they were greeted by women and welcomed to draw sweet water and replenish their provisions. It surprised them that they saw no men or boys around – but so well were they treated that they asked no questions.

One by one they were seduced and decided to stay. Even Jason forgot his mission in the arms of their beautiful queen. Only Hercules held out. He had stayed on board to guard the ship and when they did not return he stormed on to the land and hauled them out of their soft beds, berating them for being so weak and forgetful of their great purpose. Unwillingly, they sailed away. They learned later that the women of Lemnos had murdered all the men and boys on the island, determined to live without them. Realizing, after a time, that their race would die out if they did not mate with men, they had captured the Argonauts to breed from them. It is said that many, including their queen, bore children after the Argonauts' brief visit.

They stopped on the shore of the Sea of Propontis and were welcomed heartily by one of Chiron's ex-pupils, King Cyzicus. In the small hours, after a night of pleasurable entertainment, they were interrupted by an attack by monsters from the mountains. They managed to beat them off but in the confusion their friend, King Cyzicus, was killed inadvertently by one of the Argonauts. Horrified, they sailed away, but not for long. A whirlwind and a storm drove them back to shore, and the magic bough from Dodona told them they must appease the soul of Cyzicus. They gave him a noble burial on the headland and Orpheus sang his eulogy while they danced a mystic dance around the shrine of the earth goddess. Then, as was the custom at that time, games were held in his honour.

After they had laid the spirit of Cyzicus to rest, they journeyed on, always travelling east. At one point Hercules broke his oar and when they anchored for the night he went into the forest to seek suitable wood to replace it. Hylas, his squire, followed him, but paused to drink from a pool. The water nymphs saw his youth and beauty and hauled him under to be their lover. In vain, Hercules searched for him throughout the night, and when the dawn came the breeze was so fair for sailing the Argonauts argued as to whether to wait for Hercules and lose the breeze, or sail on without him. In the end they decided to sail, so for the rest of the journey they were without the strength of Hercules.

Further on, they came to a land ruled over by a king as unpleasant as Cyzicus had been pleasant. He was a great brute of a man who fancied himself as a boxer. He challenged the Argonauts to produce a boxer from among themselves who could defeat him. Up to now he had killed everyone who had come against him. Polydeuces, one of the twins, took up the challenge and succeeded in defeating and killing him. His people angrily rose against the Argonauts and they had to row away from the place in haste to save their lives.

Entering the Bosphorus was difficult; fearsome currents and winds nearly wrecked them. But at last they anchored on the shore of Bithynia, ruled by King Phineas, the blind seer. He offered to feed them, but as soon as the food was produced three ghastly creatures, half bird, half women, descended on them and tore the food away. Phineas told them he and his people were starving because these harpies had been sent to torment them.

Zetes and Calais pointed out that it might be because he had angered the gods by keeping his wife, their sister, imprisoned, and blinding her two sons on the bidding of his mistress. They demanded that he release their sister at once and allow Jason to cure the boys' eyes with a herbal salve he had to hand. This was done, and when the harpies appeared again they were chased off by Zetes and Calais who, as sons of the north wind, could fly further and faster than the harpies themselves.

At last the Argo reached the great open sea, the Euxine (known today as the Black Sea). Few Greeks had sailed this far before and they frightened each other with horrific tales about it, hugging the southern shore as best they could.

Orpheus warned them about the wandering rocks that his mother, the muse Calliope, had told him about as a child, and they soon came upon them. Huge, towering cliffs of rock appeared in the ocean, with the water surging and thundering around and between them. It seemed impossible to get past. Orpheus told Tiphys the steersman that Hera would protect them, but Tiphys could not bring himself to trust her until she sent a messenger, a heron, who led them through. Safely on the other side, but exhausted from the prodigious effort of fighting against the waves, they sought a sheltered harbour as soon as they could. They anchored at the mouth of the Wolf River – but there suffered two losses. Both Idmon and Tiphys died, one by fever and one by the thrust of a wild boar. Ancaios, the astrologer, familiar with the pattern of the stars, was chosen as steersman to replace Tiphys.

They rowed past the land of the Amazons, a fierce tribe of warrior women, who sacrificed horses on their altar of black stone, and the shores of Chalybes where black smoke betokened the perpetual fires of the furnaces that smelted the precious metal, iron, as yet unknown in the rest of the world. At last they glimpsed the tall peaks of the Caucasus Mountains at the furthest reach of the sea. There they came upon a boat adrift and in trouble. On board were the four sons of Phrixos and Chalciope, who had left Colchis in the hope of reaching their father's homeland, Greece. Jason and his companions laughed to think that such young lads in such an inadequate ship could dream of tackling the journey they had themselves just completed with such difficulty through storm, tempest and raging seas, but they took them on board kindly and told them of their mission to take the Golden Fleece back to Greece to give peace to the soul of their father Phrixos. The boys agreed to guide the Argonauts to Colchis and introduce them to their grandfather, King Aietes.

Meanwhile, Aietes in his golden palace dreamed that a star fell out of the sky into his daughter Medea's lap. She threw it into the River Phasis that flowed past his palace and it was carried away by the water and was lost in the Euxine Sea. He knew it boded ill for him and his family. Then spies reported seeing a strange, outlandish boat rowing up the Phasis. He called for his golden chariot and his two daughters, Chalciope and Medea, and rode down to meet the boat as it drew near. Around him an army of warriors was ready to attack at his command, but the command was never given because he could see his four grandsons on board.

Jason and his crew, travel-stained and exhausted from their long haul from Greece, greeted him courteously, somewhat awed by the magnificence of the welcoming party and the palace they could see in the background. Aietes replied cautiously, not pleased at all to welcome such a strange, wild bunch of men to his home. But the laws of hospitality demanded that he be civil. The men were invited to the palace where they bathed and were clad in more suitable garments before they sat down to eat. The eyes of Medea never left the handsome Jason and he, in his turn, was not unaware of her admiration, nor was he averse to it.

Because Aietes had greeted them as noble visitors in spite of their appearance, Jason thought it only right he should be straight with him, and he told his host that he had come for the Golden Fleece. Aietes' face grew dark. Angrily he replied that he would not give it up. If Jason and his men were determined to take it they must choose a champion among them who would have the courage to win it in a way that Aietes would dictate.

Jason at once volunteered, knowing that it was he who must win the fleece. Chalciope and Medea drew together, whispering, the one wishing the fleece could go to Greece to release her husband's soul from torment, the other so attracted to Jason she determined to help him no matter what the consequences.

The sons of Phrixos warned Jason not to take up the challenge.

'There is no way you can win,' they said, and told him what horrific labours their grandfather would demand of him.

Then Medea came to him secretly in the night and gave him some magic salve, which he was to rub all over himself and all over his armour.

'But the virtue of this will only last one day, so by nightfall you must have completed your task.'

In the morning his first task was to tame two bulls, yoke them, and plough a four-acre[1] field belonging to the god of war. When the furrows were clean and straight he had to sow dragon's teeth in them. The people gathered to watch, the Argonauts filled with misgiving.

But Medea's salve worked well and he was aware the bulls could not harm him. To help him further the sorceress, Medea, uttered spells to calm them down. Jason yoked them and ploughed the field, but wherever he had sown the dragon's teeth fully armed warriors sprang up and attacked him. Medea had warned him that this would happen and told him he must throw a rock into the midst of them. As soon as he did that, they fell to fighting among themselves, each accusing the other of throwing the stone. When they had slaughtered each other Jason approached the throne of Aietes and demanded the fleece.

'In the morning,' Aietes said, 'for it is almost dark now.'

He, of course, had no intention of giving up the fleece in the morning, but plotted to attack the Argo at night and massacre the crew. Medea came to Jason again and warned him of her father's intentions. She advised him to take the fleece that night and sail away before first light. She hinted that because she had helped him her father would certainly put her to death. Jason declared at once that she should come with them on the Argo and be his queen when he at last claimed his rightful throne in Iolcos. She advised him to bring Orpheus with him and at midnight she and her youngest brother, Absyrtus, met the two Argonauts in the forest.

Their first obstacle was a mighty wall, with a gate of threefold bronze guarded by a monstrous female demon. Medea made the men dig a ditch into which she led a lamb she had brought with her. She killed it and covered it with herbs and honey, and then indicated that they should watch and hide.

Suddenly the three-headed wild woman of the forest appeared, surrounded by her howling hounds, seized the lamb and took it away to eat in her lair. Quickly Medea signalled them forward to open the gate. Once through they were in the depths of the forest, but were guided by the gleam of the Golden Fleece. They found it, at last, hanging from the oak tree where Phrixos had placed it – but underneath the tree a vast and deadly snake lay coiled. Medea whispered to Orpheus, and he swung down his harp from his shoulder and began to play and sing. Slowly, slowly, the snake uncoiled, listening to the music, hypnotized by its sweetness.

Jason leapt over its vast body and seized the fleece. Before the snake could recover, they were already running through the forest, through the gate and down to the marshes that hid the Argo. Everyone was ready and waiting and, within moments, the ship slid down the river towards the sea with Medea and her young brother on board.

When Aietes realized what had happened he set off in pursuit, a formidable fleet of ships gaining on the Argo every moment. Medea, seeing that they were about to be captured, stabbed her brother, tore him to pieces and threw him overboard. The time Aietes took to gather up his son helped the Argo to escape with its precious cargo. Horrified, the crew stared at Medea. What kind of woman would do such a thing? For the first time, and not for the last, Jason shivered when he looked into the eyes of his young bride.

Then came the long journey home. The Argo was battered and worn from the storms it had endured, the men were tired and older than they were when they set off. The gods were angry with Medea for what she had done and pursued them with calamities.

At last Jason asked the magic bough for advice and was told that the Argo was now stained with the blood of Medea's foul deed. When the men heard this they wanted to throw her overboard as she had thrown her brother, but the bough warned them that they still needed her help.

They struggled through the storms, heaved themselves off sandbanks, even dragged their boat for nine days across land. They were lost and desperate. Medea guided them to her sister Circe's island where they were given food and drink. But Circe would not let them stay because of the blood that stained their boards. They were nearly seduced by the sweet songs of the sirens who lulled men to sleep for ever, but Medea made Orpheus out-sing them and they escaped at last. They were storm-tossed in the ocean that has no end, but returned at last through the Pillars of Hercules to their own ocean. There they were almost sucked down into the depths by the terrible whirlpool of Charybdis off Sicily, and attacked by the six-headed monster Scylla. Even Orpheus almost despaired of ever reaching Iolcos.

At one point they reached a city with a magnificent harbour full of tall ships. They were amazed, for when they had passed this way before it was open countryside. For the first time they realized just how many years they had been away and how old they had become.

Medea spotted some of her countrymen in the town and for a while there was a danger that she would be captured and sent back to her father for punishment. But Jason persuaded the men that they would never be able to hold such a cunning sorceress as herself for long, so they might as well abandon their instructions to capture her and settle down in this fair land out of the reach of Aietes.

When they sailed on they were driven by storms to Africa and wandered for a long while in the burning deserts. Turning north again, they came to Crete and were about to land for fresh food and water when they were attacked by a bronze giant, Talus, breathing fire. Medea insisted on going ashore by herself and, with her wiles, managed to trick him into showing her his weak spot. By using that, she drained him of all his fire and left him useless on the shore.

They rowed on and at last reached the Peloponnese. At Malea they offered sacrifices to purge themselves of the guilt they had carried all these years. Not long after this they wept to see Mount Pelion and the harbour of Iolcos. They ran the ship aground but did not have the strength to haul it further. People came running to see them, shouting with astonishment, for everyone believed they were long since dead. Sadly depleted in numbers and in energy, the aged heroes limped up to the palace of Pelias carrying the Golden Fleece. He, an old, blind, crippled man, accepted it and could no longer deny Jason the throne.

Epilogue

It is said that Medea bore Jason three children but, as the years went by, his love turned to hate and she killed them out of spite.

He died at last sitting wearily in the shadow of the Argo, dreaming of the brave adventures of his youth. The ship collapsed and buried him.

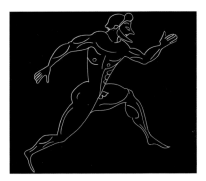

GREEK ATHLETE

Commentary

CERTAIN THEMES ARE significant in this story. One is the theme of sacrifice – the contrast of 'true' sacrifice with 'false' sacrifice.

The gods send a golden ram to save Phrixos from being sacrificed by his father. The father of Phrixos may be prepared to do the deed because he believes the gods have called for it, but in fact it is the wicked stepmother who tricks him into what is tantamount to murder. This is a false sacrifice. I find it interesting that a ram, which is usually the victim of sacrifice, becomes here the saviour. In the Hebrew religious texts, centuries later, a ram is substituted for Isaac who was also about to be sacrificed by his father.[2]

The ram that saves Phrixos is golden, suggesting something more spiritual than just the male generative force the ram usually represents in myth. Phrixos clings to its fleece (a positive act) and is taken to Colchis where he fathers children and sets in motion a train of events that will lead another virile young man to achieve great deeds. This is the destiny of Phrixos. Helle, his sister, who is not part of this destiny, should not have tried to accompany him.

The ram voluntarily gives up its life when it has served its immediate purpose. This is a true sacrifice which results in its power increasing after its death. Aietes believes the life will go out of his kingdom if the fleece is removed; the dead Phrixos believes that life in the Otherworld will be his if it is returned to his native land; Jason believes he will regain his lost kingdom and have the life destiny intended for him if he has the fleece. In each case, it is desired for something more than itself and its possession, like the legend itself, carries a significance greater than the sum of its parts.

However, in order for the Golden Fleece to be obtained there are other true sacrifices that have to be made by the Argonauts who seek its benefits – comfort, safety, home, loved ones . . . Such true sacrifices are an important part of the development of the journeying soul.

A false sacrifice crucial to the development of the story was Medea's ignoble sacrifice of her young brother. From this dark deed sprang many horrific ills for the crew of the Argo. The Argonauts, setting off fresh and innocent, had sacrificed a bull to the gods and were given fair passage. But, after the false sacrifice of Absyrtus, the gods turned against them until at last, exhausted and humbled, they offered another true sacrifice on the beach at Malea just before they reached Iolcos. It was accepted.

The quest for the Golden Fleece does not have as happy an end as we might wish. The noble energy of the youthful Jason that drove him against all the odds to win the fleece, is dissipated by his reliance in the end on a guileful and unscrupulous woman. At his moment of greatest triumph, when he has the fleece and has turned for home, he hesitates to do the right thing, and subsequently has to pay for it dearly. Until he met Medea he had done everything with honour, even to telling Aietes openly that his intention was to take the fleece. It might well have been easier, though not so honourable, to lull his host into false security and do the deed secretly in the dead of night – as he was later persuaded to do.

Jason is shocked by Medea's murder of her brother, but he does nothing. Whatever they felt, the Argonauts tacitly condoned the murder by their silence and inaction and that is why they were made to pay for it. Jason, in his blind lust for Medea, was losing those qualities that had brought him thus far: his sense of honour, self-reliance and courage. On the way to Colchis they drove the Argo straight and true to its destination, in spite of all the dangers. They travelled hopefully. But on the way back a kind of hopelessness set in. They gave up relying on themselves and did whatever Medea suggested. It took them many, many years of wandering before they arrived back home.

Another theme that is prominent in the story is that of help offered and help accepted – 'true' help and 'false' help. Jason helps an old woman over a turbulent river at great inconvenience and risk to himself. It is an act of unselfish kindness: true help. The woman turns out to be Hera, the goddess. The deity wants not only our worship, but our generosity to all living beings in the Divine Name. We remember Christ's words: 'Whosoever shall receive one of such children in my name, receiveth me: and whosoever shall receive me, receiveth not me, but him that sent me.'[3] We remember also St Christopher, who carried a child across a turbulent river only to discover on the other side that he was Christ.

Hera helps Jason on more than one occasion on the way to Colchis; he accepts her help with gratitude and wins through the most appalling difficulties. But at Colchis he accepts help from a flawed human being, a beautiful but ruthless sorceress. Her false help brings him harm and makes him ultimately fail in life although, ostensibly, he has succeeded in what he set out to do – that is, to bring back the Golden Fleece.

An important protagonist in the story is Orpheus. He, too, was a pupil of the wise Chiron and was perhaps the most spiritual of the Argonauts. In later times Orpheus became the centre of one of the major Mystery religions in Greece and Rome, a deeply gentle and spiritual figure who, in the early centuries of Christianity, was often linked with Christ. There are, for instance, many Roman mosaics in Britain depicting Orpheus with his lute playing music to the animals and trees, surmounted by the symbol of the *chi-rho*, an early Christian sigil.

It is Orpheus, with his music, who succeeds in getting the Argo into the sea at the beginning – indicating that the physical ship alone was not capable of undertaking such a journey. It had to be driven by the power of the spirit as well as muscle. It was Orpheus, as well, who brought Jason to the Oak of Dodona and suggested that he attach a bough from the miraculous tree to the ship to give it divine guidance when it was in trouble. It was Orpheus who calmed the mighty serpent guarding the fleece and allowed Jason at last to attain his goal. Even Medea with her sorcery could not help Jason with the serpent. The music of Orpheus put to rest the confusing, surging subconscious turmoil of Jason, represented by the serpent, and allowed him to act as hero, undivided from himself.

Chiron is also an important protagonist in the story. It is he, living like a hermit on a sacred mountain, the survivor of a great battle in which most of his race were killed off because of their own foolishness, who, steeped in wisdom, teaches and trains the young princes and heroes of the land. He is half man, half horse. He has the powerful instincts, loyalty, strength and swiftness of a horse, but also the capacity for reason and imagination of a man. The Argonauts would never have won through to Colchis without his teaching. They know that and it is significant that before they set off they pay one last visit to him – to pay tribute to the past before they embark on the future.

The accidental killing of Cyzicus, another pupil of Chiron's they encounter on the way, marks the cutting of the umbilical cord between master and pupil. They are now on their own and he can help them no longer.

Everything has significance in the story as it has come down to us. For example, the loss of the sandal in the turbulent river of life indicates that Jason, in preparation for his mission, has lost part of his reliance on the world and worldly things (for our shoes are a mark of worldly civilization). He is going into the adventure part shod with the ways of the world – partly as innocent and naked as the day he was born. This kind of man frightens the civilized Pelias living in his extravagant palace protected from raw, natural experience. He therefore does everything in his power to destroy him.

Though brute strength is used a great deal in the ancient journey, most of the crucial events are launched by the subtlety and cunning of the mind. Pelias traps the innocent Jason into pronouncing his own doom. But Jason outwits him by returning with the Golden Fleece. Aietes traps the travel-worn Jason into performing feats that perhaps a less weary Jason would have been able to tackle without recourse to sorcery. Because of his exhaustion he accepts the help of Medea, and so his great victory turns to dust.

The abandonment of Hercules fairly near the beginning probably indicates that on this journey brute strength by itself cannot take them to Colchis. Jason must learn to rely on spirit and mind more than on his body if he is ultimately to win through.

When Tiphys the steersman dies, the Argonauts have to proceed into the unknown, uncharted waters with an inexperienced steersman. On the inner journey of the soul there is always a time when we have to leave our guide, our guru, our mentor, and find our own way.

When the Argonauts arrive home at last everything has changed. We set off, we journey, but we can never arrive back at the beginning, because not only has the beginning moved but we are also not the same travellers who set off. The sight of the aged Jason sitting under the shadow of the rotting hulk of the Argo, dreaming of past glories, is very moving. He is killed by a fall of wood from his own ship because he cannot let go of the past.

As the story I am telling here is about the Quest I have not gone into all the sorrows that came to Jason because of his relationship with Medea. These can be easily found in any book of classic Greek legends. Suffice to say, his uncritical acceptance of her ruined his life and undid all that he had striven for. Too late, he tried to break free and it cost him the lives of his children and of the Corinthian princess whom he later grew to love so deeply.

Anyone who is interested in the story of Jason and the Golden Fleece should read Tim Severin's book, *The Jason Voyage*. Tim Severin reconstructed a working replica of a Bronze Age Greek vessel, and in 1984 twenty oarsmen rowed it all the way from Jason's home Iolcos (now Volos) in Greece to Georgia on the far eastern shore of the Black Sea, where scholars believe ancient Colchis was situated. The story had been told and retold through three millennia at least and the events described had become so extraordinary and fantastic over the years that most scholars believed it to be a myth. But Severin saw it as a legend based on a real exploit that had become embellished and exaggerated in the telling.

The book of Severin's journey describes the rigours and difficulties of the modern Argonauts, interspersed with a running commentary on the ancient tale and how piece by piece it makes sense in the light of the modern voyage. Severin dates the original journey to the mid-thirteenth century BC on the grounds that Jason fathered a son on the island of Lemnos who was to become the mature King Euneus at the time of the Trojan War. The Trojan War, in turn, has been dated by other scholars to sometime between 1200 and 1250 BC. Another piece of confirmatory evidence about the date of the story is that the name of the River Phasis in Colchis is based on an ancient name for that river. A few centuries later, the language of the district changed and so did the name of the river. In addition, a Mycenaean Bronze Age settlement has recently been discovered in the Volos area, which was exactly where Jason's home was reputed to be at the time he would have been growing up. The clan emblem of the Aeolids, Jason's clan, was a ram. And in Georgia, around the site where Aietes' palace was supposed to have been, many ram and serpent cult artefacts from the period have been found. Where Jason was supposed to have fought the fire-breathing bulls, evidence of a bull cult has been found.

Another extraordinary 'coincidence' Severin mentions is that in the Georgian area of the Caucasus, where Colchis was supposed to have been, panning for gold in the rivers until very recently has been carried out by laying a fleece in the swiftly flowing streams – thus catching the gold dust in the fleece.

3

The Journey of the Rainbow Snake

AUSTRALIA

AUSTRALIA IS RICH in the myths of the original Australians. Since the Europeans first came to the continent, the culture of the Aboriginal people has almost been lost. But, recently, realizing what the loss of such a culture will mean to the world, some new Australians have tried to understand and record something of the sacred rites and the ancient myths. Where there has been co-operation from tribal elders we have been given glimpses – but only glimpses. These have been tantalizing enough to make us mourn the passing of the ancient wisdom and more determined than ever to honour it where it still manages to survive.

This particular story is taken from *The Elements of the Aborigine Tradition* by James G. Cowan.[1] Many tribes share this myth.

A BUTCHER BIRD

The Story

WHEN THERE WAS no Time but only Dreaming, Kunukban, the Rainbow Snake, emerged from the great ocean in search of Ekarlarwan, the All-Father, the First Cause, determined to wrestle his secrets from him for the good of the people. But Ekarlarwan was invisible and did not want to be found. He sent his dog, Djaringin, to lure Kunukban away from him. Delighted to have been assigned such a task, the dog led the snake all across the country, with the great snake's body gouging out valleys and grooves for rivers and water-holes wherever they went.

THE RAINBOW SNAKE

Trick after trick the dog played on the snake, but eventually Ekarlarwan was cornered and, during the process of a powerful ceremony, the secrets were wrestled from him. These Kunukban, the Rainbow Snake, gave to the people so that they might never more fear Ekarlarwan or live in ignorance. Kunukban then travelled on across the land creating the landscape. Wherever he went the people recorded his arrival in their songs so that it would never be forgotten that Kunukban, the Rainbow Snake, had passed that way and given them the secrets of the First Cause and the laws to live by.

Ekarlarwan was angry, however, and sent out his assistant, the butcher-bird Jolpol, to try to get the secrets back before the whole world possessed them. Jolpol was as cunning as the dog Djaringin had been mischievous. He talked sweetly to the snake pretending to be his friend and then, when he was off his guard, he pushed Kunukban's head towards the fire. In the nick of time Kunukban's true friend, the storm-bird Kurukura, arrived and drove Jolpol away. With his head fire-blackened for ever, but otherwise unharmed, Kunukban and his friend Kurukura travelled on together taking the secrets of the law all over the country.

It is said they parted at last, Kurukura to make his home at Tennant Creek, Kunukban to plunge into the lagoon at Newcastle Creek and disappear from sight, but not from dreams, for ever.

Commentary

THE ABORIGINES' CONCEPT of 'Dreaming', the *Alcheringa*, is almost impossible to describe or to explain. You either feel what it means in your heart, or you don't. Certainly it does *not* mean dreaming in the ordinary, Westernized sense of the word – the nightly fantasy or illusion in a semiconscious state. To the native Australians, it existed before time and thus gave rise to the manifestations of time, but it is also beyond time and is ever-present as a deeply metaphysical and mystical reality underlying all our lives. The myth-makers of the Aboriginal tribes, as all myth-makers everywhere, found that through song and story they could present the events of the Dreaming in symbolic form and thus preserve them in the tradition of the tribe so that they would be accessible at any moment to those who needed them and who were ready to understand them.

THE RAINBOW SNAKE (ADAPTED FROM AN ABORIGINAL PAINTING OF SNAKE DREAMING)

The land of Australia is covered by a network of tribal songs describing the activities of the Ancestors and the great supernatural beings of the Dreaming, one of the most important of the latter being the Rainbow Snake. He appears in many different myths throughout the country, most of which describe his role as being essentially caring and helpful towards the human being. He creates the landscape in which they are to live by the progress of his immense body through the rock of the first earth. Rivers and water-holes spring up wherever he has been and give life. He wrestles with the mysterious, unknown, invisible First Cause to give the people some kind of meaningful law by which to order their lives. The activities of this great being are described as though they happened in the distant past and, indeed, as he is said to have emerged from the Timor Sea, he may well represent a race memory of early migrations from the East Indies. But he is with us still and at any moment may emerge to affect our lives.

Rock paintings, more than 10,000 years old, depict the Rainbow Snake and he still features today in the rock and bark paintings done by contemporary Aboriginal artists. Figure 16 (p. 31) in the book *Aboriginal Art* by Wally Caruana shows the Rainbow Snake swallowing and regurgitating people to indicate the transformation of the people from one state to another. He is also often depicted as guarding the souls of unborn children or guiding the souls of the dead. There is a case that Wally Caruana describes of a woman who died in an aeroplane which, at that instant, was flying over a whirlpool known to be one of the lairs of the Rainbow Snake. Her subsequent 'Otherworld' journey was revealed to a man in a visionary dream.[2]

Almost always the Rainbow Snake is associated with water, from gouging out the river courses with his body in the early days to lurking in present-day water-holes, or bringing violent storms and rain to parched redlands.

Having brought the secrets of the law to the people, he is often seen as its guardian. There is a story from the area of the Eighty Mile Beach, south of Broome, that tells of a boy who angered the Rainbow Snake by eating the eggs of a goanna he had killed.[3] No doubt on the grounds that this kind of act could lead to the extinction of the goanna, the Rainbow Snake rose from its lair and lashed out at the boy. In terror he and his family hid in a cave, blocking the entrance with boulders while the Great Being raged and stormed outside. When they emerged at last, he had departed but the mountain around them had been reduced to piles of jumbled rock.

In *Aboriginal Myths* by A. W. Reed we read of a similar story describing an orphan who made so much noise crying that he awakened and annoyed the Rainbow Snake. The creature swallowed the child and his grandmother, followed by any of the tribespeople who got in his way. Still hungry, he swallowed all he encountered until at last the terrified people fought back and he was slain by a hundred spears.[4] Here we have a very different picture of the great spiritual being who wrestled the First Cause for the benefit of the people, whose passage across the land grooved out the river system and gave life-giving water to the people. It sounds like the sort of folk-tale grown-ups tell naughty children to frighten them into submission, rather than an integral part of the original myth, *unless* we read it as a warning to human beings as a whole that the great creative forces of the world are ever ready to show their other side. Water gives life; flash floods bring death. Fire cooks and warms; fire burns and kills. That the orphan should meet such a terrible punishment for crying is manifestly unfair, unless the story is telling us that the orphan represents us when we have cut ourselves off from the All-Father and All-Mother and no longer look outwards to the great world full of the wonders we have been given, but howl disconsolately about our own small disappointments and miseries. If we reject the creative energy of the universe, we will fall prey to the destructive energy of the same universe. We bring down the destructive forces upon ourselves by self-pity and inaction. Once activated, that same destructive force cannot be stopped easily, affecting all around. The Rainbow Snake in this instance is apparently killed, that is, laid at last to rest. But as the timeless supernatural force it is, it cannot be destroyed. It is no coincidence that the snake symbolizes immortality as it sheds its old skin and appears revivified. Recently, the cyclone that destroyed Darwin on Christmas Day 1974 was said to have been a warning from the Rainbow Snake that the Aboriginal people should not let their culture disappear under European influence.

Not always is the Rainbow Snake seen as male or as the male generative force. There is one version of the myth in Arnhem Land that speaks of an old woman, the All-Mother, who came originally from across the sea in the form of the snake, and emerged in the Dreaming from underground with children inside her whom she released into the world.[5]

There is another Rainbow Snake story from the northern Kimberley region which tells of the Beginning. Before all else there was sky and earth. In the sky was the Milky Way; on the earth was a great snake. They dreamed, and from the dreaming of the Milky Way a spiritual force went out and projected images on to rocks and into caves. From these came living beings, peopling the earth. But it was the great snake dreaming in the earth that opened their mouths and their eyes so that they might communicate and see.[6]

We see in many of the stories that the Rainbow Snake is associated with enlightenment. He opens the eyes and mouths of the first people. He wrestles with the First Cause to bring them 'the secrets'. There are stories of medicine men who climb to heaven up the back of the Rainbow Snake, carrying the one who is being prepared for initiation. There he inserts quartz crystals into the body of the postulant who thus takes on something of the nature of the Rainbow Snake and gains access to the Dreaming.[7]

It is interesting that Australia is not the only repository of myths about the Rainbow Snake. Yves Bonnefoy quotes several from Africa. For example, the Yoruba people of West Africa describe Oshumaré, the Rainbow Snake, as one who is both male and female, a symbol of continuity. His/her strength holds up the earth and keeps it stable and whole. His/her movements draw up the water, transforming it into rain-bearing clouds. In Brazil, to which many of the African myths were taken during the time of the slave-trade, the Rainbow Snake is celebrated by swimming under a waterfall whose spray almost continually supports a rainbow.[8] In the ancient Yombe culture of West Africa and in the Zulu culture of Southern Africa the Rainbow Snake is associated with rain and storm.

The Fon peoples of Dahomey and Togo have a myth very similar to the Aboriginal one. The Rainbow Snake was the first created being and he carried the Supreme Being in his mouth on his journey around the world. Mountains containing precious gems were formed by the snake's excrement, valleys and rivers were gouged out by his bodily movements. When the earth became too heavy with all the mountains that were created, the Rainbow Snake was asked by the Supreme Being to support it. To this day the earth is supported on the coils of the Rainbow Snake. If he flexes his muscles we feel it as an earthquake.[9] If we interpret this metaphysically, rather than literally, we see it as our fate balanced precariously on the back of the *concept* the snake represents, destruction and creation lying to either side of us.

The great open spaces of Australia, much of which are desert, and which appear so blank and featureless, are actually webbed with vibrant myths and tribal song-lines, which divide the country into manageable and meaningful sections, while unifying the whole in a deeply psychic sense. The Rainbow Snake is symbolic of only one of the powerful forces at work on the landscape. When the Aboriginal goes 'walkabout', in the true sense of the word, he enters invisible fields of influence that affect his inner journey at every step, each 'field of influence' represented by an ancient tribal story-song.

We who live in overcrowded cities have long since forgotten and ignored the importance of connecting from time to time not only with the deep spiritual source of our existence, but with certain features of the natural landscape which, through millennia of sacred tradition, are capable of reminding us of that great source. Finding so many people rootless and drifting, some enterprising people are now seeking a cure by organizing 'tours', 'metaphysical adventures' and 'journeys of the heart' to many sacred sites, thereby opening themselves to the invisible fields of influence there. Sadly, these are often of necessity expensive and hurried, but there is no reason why we should not learn from the Aborigines and make sure that whenever we feel too stressed we find a hill somewhere, a riverbank sparkling with damselflies, an old ruined church or ancient stone temple and there allow ourselves time to connect with the earth and the deeply significant vibrations of the past.

4

The Journey of Merytamun to the Hall of Osiris

EGYPT

Origin

MOST OF OUR present knowledge about ancient Egyptian beliefs in an afterlife is gleaned from the elaborate collection of prayers, invocations and spells that were first carved on the walls of certain pyramids (such as the Pyramid of Unas, Saqqara *c.* 2345 BC), then painted on the inside of wooden coffins, and from the eighteenth dynasty on (*c.* 1500 BC), inscribed on scrolls of papyrus and buried in tombs with embalmed corpses.

These texts, for convenience, have most commonly been called *The Book of the Dead*, though some more properly refer to the collection as *The Book of Coming Forth by Day* or *The Book of the Great Awakening* – for they describe the soul's journey after death towards the Judgement Hall of Osiris. Osiris represents the spirit of renewal and resurrection and from his hall, if we are found worthy, we may continue a rich and satisfying life in the various realms of the Otherworld.

My story here has been drawn mostly from the following translations of these ancient texts: *The Ancient Egyptian Book of the Dead*, translated by R.O. Faulkner,[1] *The Book of the Dead: Famous Egyptian Papyri* by Evelyn Rossiter[2] and *The Egyptian Gods: A Handbook* by Alan W. Shorter.[3]

THE WEIGHING OF THE HEART. MA'AT'S HEAD IS AN OSTRICH FEATHER. ANUBIS AND HORUS HELP WITH THE WEIGHING; THOTH WAITS TO RECORD THE RESULT. AMMUT, THE MONSTER, PERCHES ON A PLINTH

The Story

I HAVE LONG been praise-singer in the temple of Amun-Ra. May the Great God not now desert me as I enter the Realms of the Dead. I feel the darkness coming upon me. At the corners of my eyes I see the darkness and fear it. I fear the darkness. I fear becoming the darkness! I fear the loss of my name in the darkness that was before any being came forth from the No-where and the No-when.

I will sing hymns that the Great Gods Ra, Osiris and Horus will hear my voice and know that I am here.

'O Living God, great Ra-Harakty, Sovereign of all the gods, Lord of Eternity who brought forth himself, Ruler of Everlastingness! All live when you rise shining in the sky.

'May all who are above and all who are below worship you, and may you be gracious to me when I depart the earth. May my name be called out to enter the solar barque that my soul may travel to every place it desires, and may I be received by Osiris in the Place of Vindication.'

The Great and Living God lifts me up. I will have courage as I journey through the West to the House of Osiris.

'Hail to you Osiris, King of Kings, Lord of Lords, Ruler of Rulers. May you grant power in the sky, might on earth and vindication in the Realms of the Dead, a journeying downstream to Busiris as a living soul and a journey upstream to Abydos as a heron.

'May you grant that I go in and out without hindrance at all the gates of the Neterworld.

'Great Horus, son of Osiris, I reach out my hand. Lead me to the seven gates, the fourteen mounds in the fourteen districts, and the twenty-one portals through which I must pass on the way to the hall of your father where wait the forty-two assessors who will judge my soul.'

The first gate is before me.

'Gatekeeper, behold me: I am come to you, innocent and void of wrong; let me not be declared guilty; let not the judgement be against me.'

One by one I name the keeper, the guardian and the recorder of each of the gates through which I must pass. Before each I prostrate myself. Before each I justify myself.

Before the first I stand. I cannot see the keeper's face. His form is constantly changing. 'I know you,' I say, 'I know your name. You are the One-whose-face-is-averted, the Many-shaped.'

The guardian hears all there is to hear. 'The Eavesdropper,' I name him.

The recorder shouts out all that passes between us. 'The Loud-voiced,' I name him.

The second gatekeeper bends over and extends his hinder parts to me. The guardian smiles and sneers and glowers and smiles again. The recorder writes with fire and I step by quickly, afraid to be scorched by his flame. I name them all according to their attributes.

The keeper of the third gate squats on the ground and eats his own excrement. The guardian stares unblinkingly at me. The recorder curses me as I try to pass.

The keeper of the fourth gate stands in silence, and there is no sound from any direction. Silently, I bow to him. 'Wakeful,' I name the guardian. 'Grim-of-visage,' I name the recorder.

'He-who-lives-on-snakes,' I name the keeper of the fifth gate. 'Fiery,' I name the guardian. 'Raging-of-power,' I name the recorder.

'The Harsh-voiced,' I name the keeper of the sixth gate. 'He-who-looks-to-and-fro-and-sees-everything,' I name the guardian. 'Sharp-of-glance, Warden-of-the-lake,' I name the recorder.

At the seventh gate I face the sternest of them all. 'He-who-cuts-them-down,' I name the keeper. 'Loud-voiced,' I name the guardian who tries to bring me down with words. But the recorder here is the defender and I pass him with a bow.

At last, rejoicing, I pass through the seventh gate. I sing, for I am becoming one with Osiris.

'I am spirit, a master of spirit, a spirit who acts.

'I have come like Horus into the holy place of the horizon of the sky; I announce Ra at the gates of the horizon, the gods are joyful at meeting me, and the costly stones of the gods are on me. The Destructive One shall not attack me, and those who keep their gates shall not be ignorant of me.'

I stand before a land of fields and mounds and rivers, a land such as I have known all my life. I enter into it. But it is not as I have known it.

'O Bestower of Powers, help me to pass through the fourteen districts of the Neterworld.'

'Back! Go back, messenger of the evil one. Have you come to seize my heart? You shall not have it. You shall not have my heart!'

I climb the first green mound, where men live on bread and beer, and ask that my bones may be knit together and my spine and my head will be firm as I stride ahead.

From the top of the second green mound I survey the Field of Rushes and perceive that the height of the barley is five cubits[4] and the emmer[5] is seven cubits. I see spirits, nine cubits tall, reaping. I see two trees of turquoise between which Ra goes forth in his golden boat. The Field of Rushes is a fair land. I long to be part of it.

The third green mound is a mound of spirits, aflame with a deadly flame. I pass by.

On the fourth mound I face twin mountain peaks that tower above me, and a snake seventy cubits long that lives by taking the heads of the dead. I rise up against him and cry: 'Cover your head, for I am hale, hale. I am one mighty of magic and sharp of eye. I am free to wander the sky while you are bound to the earth.'

I pass by.

At the fifth green mound I face spirits who would bar my way.

'Open your roads for me until I pass by you when I travel to the beautiful West. It is the command of Osiris, a spirit and a master of spirits, so that I may live by my magic power.'

At the sixth green mound I cry: 'Hail to you, cavern sacred to the gods, secret from spirits and inaccessible to the dead . . . I have come to see the gods who are in you. The slayers shall not pursue me, the adversaries shall not pursue me, and I shall live on the offerings which are with you.'

The seventh mound is the Mountain of the Rerek Snake. It lives on spirits, taking their power. I hold up my hands: 'Go back Rerek! May your bones be broken! May your poison be powerless! You shall not come against me! You shall not have me!'

The eighth green mound is the Heights of Hahotep. There the guardian, great and mighty, roars like the ungovernable waves of the ocean in storm. 'I will not be taken to the house of the Destroyer!' I cry. My magic sustains me. My god empowers me. I pass by.

The ninth mound is yellow like the desert. Even the spirits dread this place – but I speak the words I have been taught and pass by: 'Hail to you, you august god who is in your egg! I have come to you to be in your suite so that I may go in and out of your land. May I have air and power.'

The tenth is also yellow like the desert.

'You who eat what is fresh and gulp down corruption: put yourselves on your bellies until I have passed by you. No one shall take my spirit. No one shall have power over my shade, for I am a divine falcon and incense shall be burnt for me.

'I have come to you, you gods, save me and give me my powers for ever.'

At the eleventh mound I see a great town in the realm of the dead. None go out or come in, for it holds its secrets close.

'Let me pass by,' I call out, 'for I am strong by means of that Eye of Horus which lifted up my heart after I was limp.'

At the twelfth mound, which like the last one is green, my fear is great – its breath is fire, and not even the gods can get near it, nor can spirits associate with it. There are four cobras on it, whose names are 'Destruction'.

'O Mound of Wenet, I am among the Imperishable Stars. I will be with you for ever.'

The thirteenth green mound rises from a lake of fiery water.

'Hail to you, you god in the Mound of Water! I have come to you that you may give me power over water and that I may drink of the flood, just as you did for that great god for whom the Nile came, for whom herbage came into being.'

ANUBIS TENDING THE DECEASED, WHO LIES ON A LION-FORM BED

At last I reach the fourteenth – the last – yellow mound. It is the Mound of Kheraha that diverts the Nile to Busiris.

'O you gods of Kheraha, assembly which is above the flood, open your water-basins for me, throw open your waterways for me, that I may have power over water, that I may be satisfied with the flood, that I may eat grain, and that I may be satisfied with your provisions. Raise me up, that my heart may be happy!'

I come at last to the House of Osiris. There I have to pass through twenty-one portals, in each case naming the goddess who stands guard, and her door-keeper. If I fail there will be no life for me in the beautiful West, no visits back and forth to the world I have left behind. If I fail I dare not think what fate awaits me.

Before each I say: 'Make way for me, for I know you, I know your name and I know the name of the goddess who guards you.'

First I face she who is 'Mistress-of-destruction; prophetess; repeller-of-storms; rescuer-of-travellers'. 'Terrible,' I name her door-keeper.

At the second portal I meet 'Mistress-of-the-world-who-numbers-all-men'. Her door-keeper is 'He-who-fashions-the-end'.

At the third door I confront 'Mistress-of-altars, Great-of-oblations' and pass the door-keeper: 'He-who-makes-brightness'.

One by one I pass, the words of naming open door after door for me . . . until at last I enter the great Hall of Osiris, King of Eternity, Lord of Everlastingness.

I see steps leading to a raised throne at the far end. On this sits the Great God surrounded by eight columns of green malachite entwined with flowers and holding up a ceiling elaborately decorated with a vine, fat with grapes. He himself is bound closely in a garment of shining feathers, his face and hands emerging from it as green as river reeds. He wears the tall atef crown[6] and a wide, jewelled collar. His hands are crossed on his breast and he holds the crook and flail, symbols of his kingship, and the uas-sceptre,[7] symbol of his divinity. Isis and Nepthys stand behind him, slender and tall, their hands lovingly resting on his shoulders, their beauty beyond the dreams of mortal women. Before him rises a luminous lotus blossom out of which rise the four sons of Horus, the gods who watch over the entrails of the deceased.

I stare at his majesty in awe, and then turn my head fearfully to survey the great throng of gods lining the walls. Ra in all his splendour in his golden barque is there, together with the mighty Ennead, Shu and Tefnut, air and water, Geb and Nut, earth and star-rich sky. Isis is there, beloved sister and wife of Osiris, and Nepthys their sister and wife of brother Set, who slew Osiris and scattered his members throughout the length of the land. Horus the golden-winged is there, and Hathor the Lady of the Sycamores, whose milk Pharaohs drink. Forty-two gods are there. Forty-two assessors before whom I must justify myself.

I am afraid. All eyes are on me.

At the centre of the hall stands a giant pair of scales. Beside this, three figures wait silently: Thoth with his scribe's pen and palette to record the proceedings; Anubis, Lord of the Necropolis, jackal-headed; and the monster Ammut, waiting to devour me if I fail. I try not to think of the dark and noisome pit, the bottomless, nameless darkness, into which I will fall if he is given his way.

As I step forward other shadowy figures appear before the throne of Osiris. I see the bird that is my ba soul, the image of my own head upon its winged form. I see the chair on which my mother gave birth to me crowned now by the head of Meskhent, the goddess of birth. The awesome figure of Fate stands beside it. I see my shadow, my name, my ka, my akh: many of the parts of me that have separated out at death. But clearer than the rest I see my heart on the scale pan ready to be weighed against the feather of truth, with Ma'at, the goddess of truth, watching over it.

I cry out: 'O my heart of my transformation! Do not stand up against me as witness! Do not create opposition to me in the council! Do not cause the pan to sink in the presence of the keeper of the balance!'

I turn to the assessors and to each of them, one by one, I speak the words of my justification.

'O you being, broad of stride, who comes forth from Heliopolis, I have done no evil!

'O you embracer of flame, who comes forth from Kheraha, I have not robbed.

'O swallower of shades who comes forth from the cavern, I have not stolen.

'O dangerous one who comes forth from Resetjau, I have not killed men.

'O fiery eyes who comes forth from Letopolis, I have done no crookedness.

'O flame which comes forth backwards, I have not stolen the god's offerings.

'O bone-breaker who comes forth from Heracleopolis, I have not told lies.'

And so it goes on. I swear I have not been sullen, I have neither committed perjury, nor stolen bread, nor eavesdropped, nor caused terror, nor been hot-tempered. I have not been deaf to the words of truth. I have not created disturbance, or cheated, or been neglectful, or impatient, or quarrelsome. I have not reviled or blasphemed God.

At the end I cry: 'Hail to you, O you who are in the Hall of Justice, who have no lies in your bodies, who live on truth . . . save me . . . protect me, for I am pure of mouth and pure of hands!'

After this I am questioned and the questioning is long and hard.

Mercifully, I hear the words at last: 'Proceed! Behold you are announced to Him whose roof is fire, whose walls are living uraei,[8] whose floor is the primeval waters. Osiris, the Lord of Eternity, the King of Everlastingness.'

Thoth speaks and his voice is like thunder in distant mountains.

'Hear you these words in very truth. I have judged the heart of Merytamun and her soul stands up as a witness regarding her. Her character has been proved righteous upon the great balance, and she has been found without crime.'

Then the gods of the Ennead speak to Thoth.

'That which has come forth from your mouth is just. Merytamun has been proved. She is one with Osiris. Ammut shall not be suffered to prevail over her. Let there be given to her bread which has been offered in the presence of Osiris, and a portion of the land, that she may dwell in the Field of Offerings for ever.'

I am adorned with feathers by Ma'at, the goddess of truth, and led before Osiris by Horus.

The Great God looks into my eyes, and I know what is to be known.

I walk through the hall rejoicing. I come out into the fields, into the sunlight.

'O Field, I have come into you, my soul behind me and authority before me. O Lady of the Two Lands, establish my magic power for me, that by means of it I may recall what I have forgotten. I am alive without harm of any kind, and joy is given to me. Peace is mine. I receive air.'

The country of the Neterworld is rich and beautiful. I sail boats on the rivers and the lakes. I walk among the tall and rustling corn. The scent of flowers charms me. The great river flows by.

When I wish it, I may leave the fair land and sail among the stars in Ra's golden boat, or visit the land of the living, passing in and out of the door of my tomb. Eternity holds no fear for me, nor does the Everlasting have pain.

SPIRIT OF THE DEAD BEING GUIDED BY ANUBIS TO GATEWAY

$$\boxed{\textit{Commentary}}$$

FACED WITH DEATH most people are fearful, or at least apprehensive. Some might even find that the anticipation of death prevents their enjoyment of life. Many cultures therefore prepare for death with an elaborate description of a journey they believe will take place once we leave the world we know and step into the unknown. That there might be nothing, total annihilation, a sudden and devastating cessation of everything, is unacceptable to most people. The slow development and refinement of our consciousness throughout our lives, the hard-won accumulation of learning and wisdom over years of experience, combined with the deep-seated and almost unshakeable intuitive feeling that this is leading somewhere makes us reject annihilation and consider the alternative. We cannot know what the alternative is. We can only guess at it, based on our experience in this life or on the words of some great philosopher, prophet, avatar or teacher. But whatever the explanation, whatever the belief, the unknown has to be expressed through the images and symbols and metaphors of the known.

Egypt is dominated by the River Nile. Nearly all journeys are by boat downstream or upstream. The villages and the towns are built mostly along its length on high ground to escape the annual inundation, the flooding that follows the heavy rains in the mountains far to the south. It is not surprising, therefore, that a great deal of ancient Egyptian afterlife myth drew its images from the features of the natural landscape the people saw around them – the mounds that rose above the flooded fields, the flowering reeds and rushes of the riverbank, the stone-built temples with their numerous doors through which only initiated priests could pass to attend the god in the innermost, most secret sanctuary.

Because of the ancient Egyptian belief that a person consisted of nine parts, some of which were released into independence at death, they did not find it at all inconceivable that one part should spend eternity among the stars, while another inhabited the tomb and had to be supplied with food and drink, while yet another could travel on the solar boat with Ra, or walk among the fields of reeds in bliss. It was even possible for one part of the being to be reborn into the world of the living. Some Pharaohs carried the title 'Repeater of Births'.

The journey into the Otherworld is expressed in mythic form in every culture – for it cannot be expressed in any other way. The religious myths of the ancient Egyptians were as well known to them as ours are to us, and when they described what they believed would happen to their souls after death, they drew on the metaphors and symbols already incorporated in their familiar myths.

One that is particularly relevant to the Otherworld journey is the myth of Osiris, Isis and Set. The various religious centres in Egypt each had a particular myth. One that became of prime importance throughout the Two Lands (north and south) was associated at first with the city of On (the biblical name) or Heliopolis (the Greek name), now a suburb of Cairo. In this myth there were nine deities (the Greeks knew it as the Ennead). The One that came before all others was named Atum. From him emerged the pair, Shu (air) and Tefnut (water). From the union of these two emerged Geb (earth) and Nut (sky), who in turn gave birth to four: Osiris, Isis, Set and Nepthys.

Osiris and Isis, brother and sister, were also husband and wife. They ruled Khemet (the Black Land, Egypt) in the early golden days as a great king and queen. Set, jealous of his brother Osiris, contrived to murder him. He produced an exquisite jewelled coffin and declared that whoever it fitted could possess it. Set persuaded Osiris to try it and as soon as he lay in it, slammed down the lid, sealed it with molten lead, and threw it into the ocean.

Heartbroken, Isis searched for it and finally found it in the palace of the king of Byblos (near modern Beirut). The story goes that it had been washed up on the shore nearby and the trunk of a tamarisk tree had grown around it. The king had incorporated the tree as a column in his palace. Isis retrieved the coffin and took it back to the marshes of the Nile Delta. There, transforming herself into a bird, she hovered over Osiris' body, fanning it with her wings until breath returned to it. Then she lay with him and conceived their son, Horus.

Set sought out the lovers and, this time, cut his brother into so many pieces there was no way he could continue to live on this earth. The pieces were scattered. Isis searched them out and buried each piece where she found it. The head was buried at Abydos, where its presence gave this place a religious significance, greater than anywhere else in the Two Lands.

However, Set still did not triumph over his brother, for Osiris now became king of the Otherworld just as he had been king of this world – and there he ruled 'King of Eternity, Lord of Everlastingness'. He is depicted in ancient Egyptian iconography as closely bound, all his parts held together by a richly jewelled and feathered mummy cloth. He holds the crook and flail and wears a crown, symbols of kingship. He also carries the staff, symbol of divinity. His skin is usually painted green – for he, having come alive again after death to father a child, is represented by the green of herbage that comes alive again after apparently dying and being buried in the ground. In Egyptian tombs it was common to place a seed-tray in the shape of Osiris, planted with seed which grew after the tomb was sealed. His survival promised the ancient Egyptians survival after death if they could but become 'one' with him. But to achieve this they had to pass through a gruelling set of tests and examinations.

The ancient Egyptians believed in a complex and elaborate system of gods and goddesses who oversaw just about every aspect of life and death; too complex and too elaborate for us to comprehend today. There are so many pieces of the jigsaw missing. I see these gods and goddesses as 'aspects' of the unknowable, supernatural realm that humans have always sensed around them and to which they have given persona and names. The ancient Egyptian word often used for these 'aspects' is '*ntr*' (neter) and the Otherworld is sometimes referred to as the 'Neterworld'. This is something like the 'Dreamtime' of the Australian Aborigines and something like the Christian idea of heaven, purgatory and hell. It is at once the mystical reality of the inner self beyond material reality, and the world we believe we enter in spirit form after we leave the body we have known during life on earth. It is at once 'here and now', and 'there and then'. The Egyptians make a distinction between 'eternity' and 'everlasting'. I assume 'eternity' is outside time altogether – the inexpressible and unknowable reality sometimes experienced here on earth in a moment of brilliant illumination, like a sword of lightning striking the facet of a diamond. 'Everlasting' is, in a sense, a lesser concept. It is time that lasts for ever.

When entering the Neterworld at death, the first thing Merytamun does is to involve the mysterious force of Ra, believed to be behind all other forces. Ra (the sun) is the source of light for our earth and all our physical energy. The deceased asks to be ferried across to the Neterworld in the sun's golden barque where she will be protected from harm and where she will be infused with new energy so that she may live, move and go about her business as she did on earth – no longer a limp, mute corpse.

The next great invocation, the next great prayer, is to Osiris who was once a human like ourselves, but is now a 'spirit who acts'. He was a just king on earth who is now a just king of the Neterworld. The deceased asks to journey downstream to Busiris on the delta where Osiris once lived and died. She wishes to be identified with Osiris so that she too may live again, though dead.

Osiris became a living god when his head was buried at Abydos. The heron who skims over the waters of the Nile, taking sustenance from its sacred depths, and who flies into the flooded fields during the annual inundation, was associated in ancient Egyptian minds with the benu bird, a kind of phoenix which appeared on the first mound that rose above the primeval waters at the beginning of time and laid the egg of existence.

The deceased has passed through death like Osiris at Busiris but wishes to fly south to the holy city of Abydos like a heron, a living soul, reborn. Merytamun then calls on Horus, who is depicted as a falcon or a hawk in the iconography because he flies so high and sees so far, and who, in the mythology, is the son of Osiris, conceived mysteriously after the death of Osiris, thereby suggesting once again that death is not the end. He was reputed to have fought a battle with his uncle, his father's murderer, Set, lord of the deadly desert storms, and defeated him. He is therefore a fitting guide and protector for the journey of the deceased into the unknown.

The journey is a difficult and a hazardous one, involving passing through and being challenged at seven gates, fourteen mounds in fourteen districts and twenty-one portals – only to be faced, at the end, by forty-two assessors. Note that these are all multiples of seven. For some reason, the number seven has always been a very potent number and is used in sacred mysteries throughout the world. There are seven openings in the head: two ears to hear; two eyes to see; two nostrils to take in the air without which we cannot survive and one mouth to take in food and send out words . . . There are seven days of creation, seven ages of man, seven pillars of wisdom, seven wonders of the world, seven sacraments, seven virtues and seven deadly sins, seven strings to Apollo's lyre, seven pipes for Pan . . . The menorah has seven branches and the Temple in Jerusalem took seven years to build . . . Even the Ka'aba in Mecca is circumambulated seven times . . .

The ancient Egyptian belief in the reality and power of magic was very strong, and central to the efficacy of a spell was the knowledge of 'name'. The ancient Egyptians dreaded namelessness. Criminals were often deprived of their names as the worst punishment that could be inflicted – as bad as excommunication for a devout Catholic. The names of a Pharaoh who had become anathema (such as Hatshepsut and Akhenaten) were scratched off inscriptions on walls and statues in an attempt to wipe their memory from the earth and assign them to oblivion. In this century we have seen several examples of the rewriting and falsifying of history with much the same purpose in mind. People work hard to 'make a name for themselves' and that name can bring them fame or shame.

At every stage of the journey the deceased had to make in the Otherworld of the ancient Egyptians, he/she had to name the gatekeepers, the guardians, the recorders, the gods and the goddesses encountered. In this case, the naming implies knowledge. Merytamun cannot pass on to the next stage of the process towards vindication and awakening to life without knowing who and what she is facing. The knowledge, the understanding of a truth is the only key that will open the way forward. And every truth faced, and ultimately learned, has several aspects. That is why there is more than one name to find at each gate, mound and portal. There is also a sense in which knowing the name of someone gives the knower a certain amount of power over that person (and there is a myth about how Isis tricked Ra into giving her his secret name). Having once learned it, she used it against him. By knowing the names of the gatekeepers Merytamun, the deceased, has confidence to go on. She has gained power. The wild and mysterious nature of reality has somehow been tamed. She has 'a handle on it'.

Ancient Egyptian hieroglyphs have only recently been deciphered. Jean Champollion's big breakthrough, with the aid of the Rosetta Stone, was in 1822–4. Since then, a great deal of work has been done on translating the texts. I have consulted several translations and found the variations not at all surprising, given the difficulty of the work. The language had no written vowels, for instance, or punctuation. They wrote from right to left or left to right, up or down, depending on how the hieroglyphics looked. Design and harmony were all important. The names of the different gatekeepers, guardians, recorders, etc., are often very puzzling. I wonder sometimes if they have been translated correctly even in the most authoritative texts. I have chosen to use the least puzzling here, but have to admit I am still stumped for an explanation in many cases.

At each gate the deceased pleads for mercy and justice, and describes herself so that 'those who keep their gates shall not be ignorant' of her. Then she names the three she finds at each gate to show that she is not ignorant of *them*. That there are three reminds me of the Hegelian concept that progress occurs because of the dynamic process and interaction of 'thesis; antithesis; synthesis'. The magical number three is represented by birth, death, life; past, present, future; mother, father, child . . .

I see the keeper as the prime aspect of reality to be considered at that particular moment. For instance, the first represents constant change. The second represents the aspect of reality we have avoided looking at before: the hidden 'hindquarters', as it were. The third represents our need to re-examine what we had rejected in life. The fourth shows the silence in which truth comes to us: the recognition that words cannot give us understanding. What does the fifth represent? The snake is the power of the hidden, the secret – that which lurks in our subconscious and which can kill us if we do not see it. The sixth is the shaper of events: destiny. The seventh is the sternest of all: 'he-who-cuts-them-down'. I think this represents the cutting away of all the deceased's 'ego-baggage' so that she may enter the next phase of the journey unencumbered.

The guardians are there as a warning of what can happen if the deceased cannot 'name', cannot understand. The guardians watch, listen, observe and sometimes they even try to put the deceased off the mark. The recorders are there to remind us that everything we do, everything we are, is being recorded – and not always by a sympathetic scribe! Nothing we do, say or think will ever be forgotten.

When Merytamun reaches the last gate, having successfully stood up against mockery, cursing, threats, fiery blasts and raging power, she realizes that the hostility she encountered was not hostility at all but the stern working of justice. Once she has passed all the tests, that which appeared to threaten her now becomes her defender.

She passes through the seventh gate relieved and happy. The reference in her hymn of rejoicing to 'the costly stones of the gods' is probably to the talismans of precious stones, each representing a deity, folded in to the winding sheets of the deceased's mummy – the very same precious stones that tomb robbers through the centuries have desecrated the graves to steal. As Merytamun steps through the seventh gate she sees a landscape before her, and she knows she will have to face many more dangers before she reaches Osiris.

To the ancient Egyptians the receptacle of consciousness was the heart, not the brain. It was the heart that was weighed against the feather of truth in the Halls of Osiris. It was the heart that must be protected at all costs. 'Back! Go back, messenger of the evil one. Have you come to seize my heart? You shall not have it. You shall not have my heart!'

Merytamun steps forward and finds that as she walks through the mysterious country she has entered she encounters fourteen mounds, and at each she has a significant experience. The mound was of great importance in ancient Egyptian religious mythology, for it was believed that it was the rising of a mound of earth out of the primeval waters which signalled the Beginning. No doubt this potent image came from observing the importance of rising ground during the time of the annual inundation of the fields when the life-giving silt was deposited. However, it also suggests height above the mundane: the vantage point from which we can see much further than normal. Most of the mounds are green, suggesting that they are placed among verdant fields. Several are yellow; I assume these refer to the desert, which is never far away in Egypt.

At the first mound Merytamun asks for the solidity of her body to be returned to her, for without it she will not be able to walk forward. It seems she is still in a realm close to the mundane world and the spirits she meets there feel the need to eat bread and drink beer as they did on earth. I am reminded of present-day psychics who claim to put us in touch with our dead relatives and who decribe the Otherworld as very much like our own. 'Auntie Grace is worried about her little dog . . .' 'Grandpa asks what happened to his favourite pipe . . .' The Otherworld comes across as a sort of suburbia in the sky. This used to make me dismiss the whole concept of another world as ridiculous, but now I see it as the confusion of souls recently departed from this earth but still clinging to old memories before moving on.

From the top of the second mound Merytamun looks forward into the distant realms beyond. The Field of Rushes, or Field of Reeds, is the name given in a great many of the texts to this important part of the Neterworld and is reminiscent of the Elysian Fields of the ancient Greeks, the Fortunate Isles of the Celts, and the Paradise of Islam, Israel and Christianity. It is like earth – but better. The fields are more fertile, the grain grows higher. The people she sees are idealized humans, not aliens. She yearns to be in this fair land, but she is not ready yet for it. Having glimpsed the perfect world she aspires to, she is plunged into a series of testing encounters, each one of which has the potential to destroy her chances of ever reaching the sacred country.

The third mound is aflame with the deadly purifying fire that many religions believe we must go through to burn off the dross of our former lives. The fourth has gigantic peaks to scale by personal effort, and a horrific snake from the underworld of her own psyche to defeat. The fifth is inhabited by spirits who try to bar her way. And so it goes on: one dangerous challenge after another. She meets them all with courage, calling on the neters she believes in to sustain her; she announces to all who accost her that the power of the neters is already within her. If she falters for a moment, losing faith in the neters and in herself, she will be lost. She knows it and does not falter. She has remembered the teaching about the gods she learned when she walked on the earth and she quotes it haughtily, proudly, outfacing her enemies. She has been made strong by her belief in the Eye of Horus – the same eye Horus sacrificed in order to avenge his father Osiris. This is the same blazing eye that sees everything and cannot be deceived.

The fourteenth mound is in the desert, a yellow mound. In the desert the importance of water is more evident than anywhere else. At the fourteenth mound she asks that she may have power over water, for without water life is not possible. The water she requests is, of course, not only the liquid we drink on earth but the primeval waters from which all life came: the waters of spirit, the waters of the sacred lakes around the temples, the holy water that cleanses and heals the spirit, the water that baptizes and initiates, the water that surrounds the foetus and pours out on to the earth when a child is born . . .

She comes at last to the House of Osiris. But before she enters she must pass through twenty-one portals. The House is like the temples she has known on earth; a vast place with many secrets, many doors and many chambers. The Hall of the God is in the furthest hall, the most secret, the most inaccessible.

At each portal, each door, she must name two beings – the goddess who stands guard and her door-keeper. Before each Merytamun says: 'Make way for me, for I know your name and I know the name of the goddess who guards you.' Again, knowledge of what she is encountering and an understanding of this stage of her initiation is essential.

At first she feels fear, but she must keep her courage. At the second she sees the vast hordes of humans who have lived and died and knows that all are 'numbered' individually, and that all are controlled by destiny. At the third she understands the importance of ritual observances: the 'brightness' that comes to the heart from honouring the gods. At the fourth and fifth more of the ego-baggage she has carried in her life is burned away, and she reaches another level of wisdom. She has to face darkness, attack, loud and reverberating voices.

From the twelfth door on, the door-keepers are not mentioned. Merytamun has come very close to the inner sanctuary of Osiris. The female neters who guard the doors are high-ranking – directly under the supervision of the highest. On earth, the High Priest daily clothes and feeds the statue of the god believing it to be inhabited by the spirit of the god. Here in the Otherworld much the same happens. The High Priest (who must, of course, himself be a god) veils 'the Limp One'. Osiris is the Limp One for he, at this point, represents the unrisen dead. The High Priest keeps him veiled until the moment has come for him to reveal himself in glory as the ever-living, Lord of Eternity and Everlasting.

At the twelfth and thirteenth portals Merytamun experiences illumination and welcome, a respite from challenge and confrontation. But at the fourteenth, fifteenth, sixteenth, seventeenth and eighteenth, she is again subjected to horrifying tests. If she does not waver she will pass through to the nineteenth where she will encounter the magnificence of dawn – the blazing light of rebirth. The goddess who greets her has the wisdom of Thoth (Djehuti, the god whose book contains all knowledge and all wisdom from the beginning to the end of time). At the twentieth, the darkest, deepest secrets are revealed to her.

Merytamun comes at last to the twenty-first portal where, if she falters or wavers or fails, she may yet be destroyed before she enters the sacred Hall. This goddess is of such high rank no one may know under whose orders she is acting. One suspects that she might have a higher authority even than Osiris.

Almost all descriptions of the world after death have a judgement element. Whether we like it or not, at one point, we have to face up to what we have done and what we are. The journey that is described as taking place in the Otherworld is actually, also, a cunning device for making us look at the journey we are making here and now, still in the body. Day by day in the material world we have to make decisions that are poised between good and evil. Day by day we face spiritual as well as physical dangers. Day by day everything we do is judged – if not by the forty-two assessors in the Hall of Osiris, or by Christ on the throne at the right-hand of God the Father, then by our contemporaries, our descendants, our own consciences.

The myth of the Otherworld journey holds up a mirror to our spiritual journey in this world. It is a magic mirror because it does not show us what our physical eyes can see as ordinary mirrors can, but it shows us what we really are when we have stripped away all subterfuge, illusion and disguise. It shows us that which we feel to be there with the deepest levels of our consciousness – but which has no form we can imagine unless we do so by metaphor, symbol and analogy.

At last, Merytamun enters the great Hall of Osiris where the final judgement will take place. His throne is raised on a dais as reference to the first mound that rose out of the primeval waters. The columns of green stone, the entwining flowers and hanging grapes all remind us of the burgeoning fertile life that Osiris represents. He is bound in mummy cloth because in the myth he was dismembered and had to be bound together again. The cloth is made of shining feathers because he is a spirit. The soul was often represented in Egyptian art as a human-headed bird. His skin is leaf-green, or, sometimes, black, to represent the life-giving silt of the inundation. Behind him stand his loving sisters, the great goddesses, Isis and Nephthys. Isis is also his wife. Note that these two also appear among the forty-two assessors who will judge Merytamun. They appear in two places at once because that is what such spirit-beings can do.

The lotus is a natural symbol for the spirit because it is rooted in mud, rises through water, and blooms with exquisite and almost unearthly beauty above in the air. In Egyptian burial ritual the viscera of the deceased were removed in the embalming process but not thrown away. They were placed in a Canopic jar and buried with the coffin. Each vital organ was protected by a separate god, usually carved on the lid of the jar. They represented four vital aspects of Horus, the son of Osiris.

The forty-two assessors corresponded to the forty-two districts of Egypt, each embodying the particular religious myth of its district. As Merytamun surveys the Hall of Osiris in awe she has a vision of the whole complex, but subtle, religious belief system of her people. At that moment myth becomes reality for her and she realizes the seriousness with which the actions of her life will be taken in this powerful and awesome realm.

As she denies sin after sin, answers question after question, her heart is weighed against the feather of truth (the feather which, in iconography, is always depicted rising from the head of Ma'at, the goddess who represented cosmic harmony and order, truth and justice).

Djehuti (Thoth) presides over the whole proceedings. He was the god honoured particularly by scribes, for he carried a pen and writing tablet to record every detail. He was also the god who inscribed the names of the justified dead on the leaves of the sacred persea tree. And it was he who presided over the trial of Set when he was accused of fratricide.

If, after all this, Merytamun is pronounced pure then her triumph over death is complete and she passes on to become a shining spirit, capable of life in many realms.

5

Kivanga's Journey to the Underworld to Bring Back His Twin

WEST AFRICA

I FOUND THIS story in a book by Yves Bonnefoy called *American, African and Old European Mythologies.*[1] It originated, according to Bonnefoy, among the Bantu people at Maycombe within the Congo region of West Africa.

The Story

BEFORE PEOPLE AS we know them today existed, very different beings walked the earth. One of these, Kivanga, felt lost and lonely, for his twin sister had been given in marriage to one of the cannibalistic Nzondo who lived in the Underworld.

Kivanga tried to enjoy life without her, but found that the food he lifted to his mouth with his twenty-four fingers had no savour, and that the rain which fell on his giant head gave him no relief from the burning sun. His sighs snapped the trunks of trees in the forest as though they were twigs, and the creatures of the undergrowth pleaded with him to seek his sister so that he might stop putting them in such danger with his sighs. But without their persuasion Kivanga had already resolved to do so.

TWINS

He chose eight companions he could trust, and set off on the long and difficult journey to the Underworld. They climbed mountains and crossed rivers but always kept moving westwards – for it is in the west that the sun sinks and enters the Underworld.

All the time they ran, the companions sang.

At last they came to the great shimmering sheet of water that divides the one world from the other. There they paused – for to cross this water took more courage than any of them knew they possessed.

Kivanga stood upon the shore and raised his arms. This was not the ocean in which he and his sister had bathed as children. This was the water that was before the First Things. To step into this was to risk everything.

'Let us call to your twin,' one of his companions urged. 'She may hear you and come to you.'

'If we step in, we may never step out,' another said.

'I can fight any warrior on dry land,' a third spoke up. 'But I cannot swim.'

'There will be no swimming,' Kivanga said, 'for this is not the ocean we played in as children. I will call – but I do not think she will hear.'

Then Kivanga raised his mighty voice and the sky rang like a gong.

Those creatures who heard him wept at the loneliness and longing in the sound.

No ripple disturbed the water before him. No answer came to his call.

He looked each one of his companions in the eye, and each one then knew that he would not give up the journey until he had been reunited with his twin.

He stepped forward.

One by one they followed him, gripping their weapons, singing the song of warriors going into battle.

Kivanga felt nothing as his foot touched the water between the worlds. It was as though there was nothing there. He looked around himself and thought at first that nothing had changed. His companions were behind him, singing boldly but gazing around themselves in nervous bewilderment. They were among fields and forests and mountains as they had been before. It was all so familiar and yet – and yet there seemed to be a subtle difference, a strange, haunting 'otherness' about the place he could not have explained or described.

He straightened his shoulders and clutched his assegai more tightly. He beckoned to his companions to move forward. As they did so, they found themselves confronting a huge door set in walls so thick and high not even a gazelle could leap over them. It was made of the mighty trunks of hardwood trees, studded and hinged with bronze, and its surface was carved with a myriad leering faces staring at Kivanga and his companions.

A MASK BASED ON A TRADITIONAL DESIGN FROM WEST AFRICA

The warriors sang louder to cover their fear, as Kivanga examined the door to see how it could be opened. There was no handle. No catch. No lock. It was a door meant not to be opened.

Several of the companions suggested they should retreat while the others looked fearfully over their shoulders, wondering how they could go back when the water they had stepped through was no longer there.

'If we are to open this,' Kivanga thought, 'we will have to use magic.' And out of a pouch at his side he took a small cult figure made from the white river clay of his home village.

He held it up to the door.

'Mbenza,' he declaimed. 'Master of the earth! Great Being beyond all beings! Give me the strength to open this door – for my twin sister is unhappy and I feel her unhappiness. I am unhappy, and she feels my unhappiness.'

The image in his hand trembled, for the great god understood unhappiness. Had he not been lonely before he created the world?

The companions, seeing the image shaking, took heart and sang louder than ever. It was no longer a battle song – but a song of power for the earth.

The earth moved and the door swung open.

Singing in triumph, the little band of warriors passed through.

Before them they saw a landscape that was dark, yet its features were somehow visible. It was frozen, yet it did not freeze them. They ran in step with the rhythm of their song and passed deep into the Land of Mystery until they came to the village of the Nzondo. They paused and looked down on it from a hill. They saw the creatures moving about; the women grinding corn; the men sharpening assegai tips. The companions no longer sang, but at Kivanga's command stayed silent, scarcely daring to breathe. He stared into the village, watching every movement. At last he saw his twin sitting by the ashes of a cooking-fire, her shoulders bent, her eyes on the ground. He longed to rush in and sweep her up in his arms, but he knew the Nzondo were strong and vicious and might soon overpower his small band.

He thought deeply, his great head in his hands. Then he whispered to his companions. Very slowly, very quietly they began to sing again. At first they sang so softly that not even they could catch the sound, then gradually, gradually they increased the volume. The ground began to vibrate as though there were drums being beaten in caverns deep under the ground. One or two of the Nzondo paused in what they were doing and looked up, but the sound was such that it made them feel sleepy. One by one they yawned and stretched and fell down where they were, fast asleep. Only Kivanga's twin did not sleep. She recognized the song of her people and she lifted her head to listen. She wept with joy when she saw her brother coming towards her – his huge, ungainly figure was the most beautiful sight she had seen in a long, long time.

The companions stayed on the outskirts of the village, still singing, while Kivanga and his sister were reunited.

'Come,' he said. 'We must go. The song cannot hold them for ever.'

He took her hand.

'Wait,' she said. 'There are things we must take with us.' And she led them to the chief's hut. Inside the dim interior he could see that the walls were hung with masks.

'See,' she said. 'My husband's people stole these from Mbenza, the Master of the earth. We must take them back. With these masks the people will become who they were meant to be.'

Kivanga helped her load the masks into a cloth, which she hung on her back.

They heard a sound outside the hut. The Nzondos were beginning to wake.

'Hurry!' he whispered. And they ran.

Seeing that their enemies were waking, the companions gripped their assegais and changed their song to one of battle, but as soon as Kivanga and his twin were with them they turned and ran back the way they had come. The Nzondo pursued, yelling imprecations and throwing their spears.

The door was still open and they rushed through, Kivanga helping his sister who was staggering under the weight of the masks. Then he turned and put his great weight against the door. At last, with a groan, it moved and creaked shut, closing them off safely from their angry pursuers.

Kivanga lifted the burden from his sister now that he no longer had to be prepared to fight and, hand in hand, they stepped into the water that was between the worlds and emerged in their own land. There, Mbenza rewarded them for the return of the masks and founded the first village of humans as we know them today.

But humans are never safe from the revenge of the Nzondo and the masks must be used in sacred rites continually, to hold the dark forces at bay. Underworld spirits lurk under pebbles, seeking to blind and paralyse their enemies, to break bones and deform limbs. The priests of Mbenza with their allies, the water spirits, have to work hard to counteract their malice and keep the human form intact.

Commentary

MANY AFRICAN MYTHOLOGIES assume that the first beings were deformed versions of the human race and had to undergo transformation with the help of some hero or heroine. In the case of Kivanga, it is significant that the human race comes into existence as a result of a being who was sundered and made whole again. Kivanga and his twin cannot be happy, cannot be whole, without each other. Nor can we exist without the union of the 'yin and yang' (to borrow terms from the Chinese), the masculine and feminine, the positive and negative, the spiritual and the material parts of ourselves. The loneliness we feel when we are sundered, and the efforts we have to make in order to bring ourselves back into a state of wholeness, are prodigious. Kivanga has to use physical prowess, mental agility, magic, courage and persistence. He must not give in to his own doubts and the persuasion of others. He must not despair. He must remember the religious teaching of his people. The image made from the white river clay of his home village combines the power of the natural forces from the earth with the power of the supernatural forces symbolically represented by the god Mbenza to open the door – the door which is there as much for our protection from a world we are not yet ready to confront, as to keep us out of a world that is not yet prepared to accept us.

Note the continuous ritual chant of his companions, the song that is also a magical incantation. According to Yves Bonnefoy[2] many African people (for example, in the Mande region) believe that the universe came out of a word from the creator God. 'In the beginning was the Word,' said St John in the Bible.[3] 'In the beginning was the Big Bang,' say the modern astronomers. There seems no doubt that vibrations set off by sound have played, and still do play, an important transformatory role in the universe. The songs of Kivanga and his companions are crucial.

The attitude to twins in African society has as many variations as there are tribes on the huge African continent. But they are never ignored or taken for granted. Often in Central and West Africa they are considered 'sacred monsters'[4] and expected to mediate between nature and supernature, and between humans and animals. The story of Kivanga and his twin draws on this idea. The Fon of Dahomey have a myth about twins born to the primordial Mother from whom, in their turn, seven pairs of twins are born to become the pantheon of local gods. In Southern Africa, however, twins were often viewed as dangerous aberrations of nature and one of a pair of twins put to death.

Before the Europeanization of Africa, carved and painted objects were not seen as art, but as vital functioning parts of a living ritual. The masks now hung in museums and galleries were not made to be so displayed, but to be used in magical ceremonies and, in many instances, they have become so impregnated with the feelings engendered at these ceremonies that they are not comfortable ornaments to have about the home.

Masks are used for the transformation of one form into another. A man who is seen around the village as an ordinary family man becomes a frightening supernatural being when he dons the mask of his calling as witch-doctor or medium. Conversely, Kivanga's people become like ordinary people of today by donning Mbenza's masks. The implication is that what we consider to be our normal faces these days are actually masks behind which our true selves are hidden. No wonder we find it so difficult to recognize each other for what we are and to read each other's minds! Serial killers still get away with their terrible murders for so long because, sitting beside them on the train or standing beside them in the street, we are fooled by their innocent looking 'masks'. Increasingly, as the power of the television image grows, we may vote into power those politicians with the most attractive masks rather than those with the most worthy policies.

The use of carved and painted masks in traditional rituals is to recall the mythic events of the early stages of existence, in order to understand and control better the events of the present. The priest or shaman takes on the persona of the ancient mythic being by covering himself with the symbols of the story he is re-creating. Note that this is re-creating, not enacting. This is not drama, but magic. Paradoxically, by putting on the mask of an ancient mythic being, he is actually taking off the mask of his everyday persona and, in so doing, he is free to act, once more, in the supernatural realm of the 'first days'.

THE DONNING OF A MASK

6

The Quest for the Holy Grail

EUROPE

Origin

MY RETELLING OF the main theme of the Grail legend here is, of necessity, very brief and bald. Since Chrétien de Troyes wrote down an ancient tale, *Le Conte del Graal*, in France in 1185, and Wolfram von Eschenbach wrote *Parzival* in *c.* 1211, countless versions have been told. Even today we have had films that have entertained millions by drawing their inspiration from the legend. These include, for example, *The Fisher King*, which starred Robin Williams, and *Indiana Jones and the Last Crusade*, starring Harrison Ford and Sean Connery.

The stories were first written down mainly in the Middle Ages and draw their imagery from this era. The Middle Ages was a time when the relics of saints, small pieces of bone, skulls, pieces of wood supposedly from the Cross on which Jesus was crucified, etc., were believed to have magical and miraculous properties, so it would not be unfitting to compare the Grail legend with a reliquary in which a sacred mystery is kept – the casket or reliquary itself becoming more and more elaborate over the centuries as successive generations of story-tellers add encrusting jewels and exquisitely enamelled panels. It is still the centrepiece that has the power to affect our lives, but we are attracted to it by the decorated casket refashioned the better to accommodate our expectations.

I have chosen to follow the German version, Wolfram von Eschenbach's *Parzival*, most closely, though I am aware of, and have used, other versions. Literally hundreds of books have been written about the search for the Holy Grail, the Arthurian cycle of stories being particularly rich in these. It is not only Perceval who seeks the Grail, but many other knights, including Sir Gawain and Sir Lancelot. All fail who have not reached the necessary standard of excellence and purity.

The Story

IT IS SAID that Lucifer, an archangel, rebelled against Almighty God and was driven from heaven. As he plummeted through the dark a brilliant emerald stone fell to earth from his crown. From this a sacred chalice was carved, the same the Lord Christ drank from at the Last Supper, the same in which his uncle, Joseph of Arimathea, was said to have caught the drops of blood that fell from the Son of God on the Cross.

After the crucifixion many of Christ's followers fled or were murdered. Joseph of Arimathea was flung into prison on suspicion of having stolen and hidden the body of Jesus. There he was secretly fed and sustained by the chalice he had hidden upon himself. His wounds were healed; his youth renewed.

Many years later the Roman emperor Vespasian, worried about the ill health of his son Titus, heard about Christ and the miraculous healings he had performed when he was alive. He sent ambassadors to Jerusalem to find out more. There they met a Christian woman, Veronica, who showed them the cloth with which she had wiped the face of the Saviour. Imprinted on it were the features of her Lord. When the ambassadors took this back to Rome and showed it to the emperor and his son, Titus was immediately healed. Intrigued, Vespasian and Titus now visited Jerusalem themselves to seek the body of Christ. They were told that the body had disappeared after the crucifixion and that Joseph of Arimathea, a rich merchant related to the criminal, had stolen it. They sought the prisoner in his cell and were astonished to find that after all those years in prison he was still strong and healthy. Vespasian ordered his release.

At once Joseph, his sister and her husband and several followers, fled the country. At first they settled in France near Marseilles, but later moved on to Britain where it is believed to this day that St Joseph of Arimathea founded the first Christian church in Britain at Glastonbury, Somerset. At first the chalice, now thought of as the Holy Grail, sustained them through all their vicissitudes, but later, as men became more corrupt and no longer worthy of it, it disappeared.

Meanwhile, a virtuous man who had accompanied Vespasian to Jerusalem had laid a crucifix of pure gold upon the altar at the Holy Sepulchre in order to pray for a son. This prayer was granted and he named his son Titurel. When Titurel grew to manhood he experienced a vision which directed him to seek and find the Holy Grail, whose guardian he had been chosen to be. He was warned by an angel that only the pure might catch a glimpse of the holy vessel and so he must be careful that he himself lived a pure and blameless life.

A mysterious white cloud led him through forests and over rivers until he reached a remote and towering mountain. Gazing upwards at its almost unscalable heights, he caught a glimpse of the green, translucent vessel hovering high above the topmost peak. Almost immediately it disappeared, but he knew that this was the Grail. He established himself on Montsalvach, the sacred mountain and, with the knights who gathered to support him, he held it against the attacks of robbers and Saracens. The mountain-top consisted of a huge boulder of onyx. He levelled and polished this, determined to build a worthy temple for the Grail upon it. The plan for the temple appeared as if by magic on the onyx foundation, and the work began. At last the most magnificent temple the world had ever known was complete. Seventy-two octagonal chapels surrounded the centre, which was vaulted with sapphire, the sun and moon represented by topaz and diamond. The windows were of transparent stones sliced thinly, beryl and amethyst and agate, and the floor was of translucent crystal under which could be seen the fishes of the ocean. The towers were of gold and precious stones. At the top of every tower, upon a crystal cross, rested the carving of an eagle with wings outstretched as though it were in flight. At the top of the tallest tower a brilliant red gem shone out to guide all the knights of the Grail homeward. In the centre of this wonderful building stood a miniature representation of the whole in which the holy vessel itself was to be kept.

When the temple was complete the priests set about consecrating it to its great purpose. At the height of the ceremony the Grail itself appeared, hovering in the air, and at last lowering itself to rest upon the altar. There it stayed, sustaining the knights who protected it, and from time to time revealing the will of God in letters of fire around its rim.

For 400 years Titurel protected the Grail and grew no older, and then one day, the letters of fire commanded him to leave the temple and seek a wife that an heir of his might inherit the task he had so ably carried out for so long. His choice fell on a Spanish princess, Richonde, who bore him a son, Frimontel, and a daughter, Richonde. Frimontel in turn had two sons, Amfortas and Trevrezent, and three daughters, Herzeloide, Josiane and Repanse de Joie. When Titurel felt that he was no longer young and vigorous enough to guard the Grail adequately, he appointed his son Frimontel in his place.

Frimontel, unlike his father, grew restless and rode out into the world where he was killed in battle. His son, Amfortas, took his place as the Grail guardian but he too left his task in search of worldly adventure. He was wounded by a thrust of a poisoned lance, and returned to Montsalvach where the years passed in great agony. The wound never healed, for it had not been received in defence of the Holy Grail but instead for the desire of a woman.

His grandfather, Titurel, wept to see his suffering and prayed that it would be lifted. One day, letters of fire appeared on the rim of the sacred chalice promising that Amfortas, the Grail King, would be healed at last when a certain chosen hero would come to the mountain and ask what had caused his suffering. After this, all lived in anticipation of the great day when this would come about.

Meanwhile, the sister of Amfortas, Herzeloide, had married and given birth to a son called Parzival. After the death of her husband in battle she retired deep into the forest and brought her son up in solitude, far from the violent ways of the world. When he was almost grown he chanced to meet some knights in shining armour in the forest and fell down at their feet, believing them to be the angels his mother had told him about. Laughing heartily at the lad's ignorance, they soon told him stories of the big world outside the forest and suggested he should ride out and join the gallant knights of King Arthur's Round Table. Very excited, Parzival told his mother about the encounter and insisted on following their advice. Unwillingly, she fitted him out for the adventure, giving him bad advice on how to behave, a shabby nag to ride and ridiculous garments – hoping that he would not get far before the mockery of others would drive him home to her.

A KNIGHT IN CHAIN-MAIL

Nothing daunted, Parzival rode out, full of joy. His first adventure involved a lady he saw sleeping in a tent in a meadow. His mother had always been pleased when he kissed her, so he was astonished that when the lady awoke she was angry because he had kissed her. Parzival told her he had meant no harm and, sensing that he was but a simpleton who indeed meant no harm, she gave him her bracelet as sign she had forgiven him. However, when she later told her husband about the amusing incident he flew into a rage and set off to pursue Parzival in order to exact revenge.

In the meantime, the youth had encountered another lady, this one weeping over a slain lover. He listened to her story and promised to punish the Red Knight who had killed her husband.

Later, faced by a wide river, he paid the ferryman with the bracelet he had received from the lady he had kissed, and came at last to the city of King Arthur. There, at the gate, he met the Red Knight carrying a golden goblet. The knight asked him mockingly where he was going. Boldly, Parzival replied: 'To King Arthur's court to ask him for your armour and your steed!' The knight laughed and let him ride on.

As the ungainly youth rode into the city the local boys clustered around him, jeering at his outlandish appearance. One of Arthur's squires took pity on him and led him to the court where, in wonderment, Parzival gazed at the rich and magnificent assembly of knights. At last he was brought before Arthur and lost no time in asking for the arms and steed of the Red Knight. It seemed the same knight had just insulted Arthur and his queen by seizing Arthur's golden cup and spilling the contents over the queen. Without giving a thought to what he was saying, Arthur told the boy angrily that he could have the Red Knight's horse and armour if he could win it. Eagerly, Parzival rode out on his sorry nag to challenge the Red Knight. Thinking to despatch the troublesome youth with one blow, the knight raised his sword. But it was not so easy. Parzival, with extraordinary zeal, surprised his opponent with many an unexpected thrust and parry. At last the Red Knight lay dead at his feet; Parzival seized his steed and his armour, pulling the latter on over the motley clothes his mother had given him, and handing the squire who had helped him the stolen goblet to return to the king, while he rode off to seek further adventure.

For a while he succeeded in the tasks he tackled more by accident than design because, although he was now caparisoned as a knight, he had no idea what was expected of him as such. At last an elderly knight befriended him and took it upon himself to train the boy in all the rules of chivalric encounter. When he rode out again he was much better prepared to meet the world.

A CHALICE

Before long, he was called upon to defend a queen in her castle and at the end, when she was safe, she offered herself in marriage. For a while he lived very happily with her, but then, remembering his mother and how pleased she would be to see him in his present goodly circumstances, he set off to fetch her.

On the way he came to a lake set in a desolate land where he found a fisherman dressed like a nobleman who directed him to a castle where he might find shelter. The drawbridge was lowered and Parzival was welcomed warmly by the inhabitants. Grateful but puzzled, he accepted all that was done for him. He was led into a great hall where 400 knights sat silently, as though waiting for a meal. Parzival could not help but notice that all who looked at him seemed pleased and expectant, as though they were waiting for him to do or say something. He kept silent, however, gazing around himself, not wanting to cause offence to anyone by his curiosity.

He was led to a chair beside the king, who sat hunched among furs, as though he were in great pain. To his surprise, Parzival recognized him as the richly clad fisherman he had seen on the lake. The king handed him a noble sword of exquisite workmanship, indicating that it was his to keep.

Suddenly the great doors opened and a procession entered bearing a lance dripping with blood. All the knights sighed deeply as it passed them. Parzival sighed too, out of politeness – but asked no questions. Next came a procession bearing a platter on which there lay the severed head of a man. No sooner had this procession left the hall, than another entered, this time a party of beautiful young women, walking two by two, carrying various objects – among them an embroidered cushion and an ebony stand. They laid these before the king. Last of all came one more beautiful than the rest, carrying a glowing chalice which she, too, laid before the king. Parzival heard the whisper that passed among the knights that this was the Holy Grail, and was then astonished to see a stream of food and drink pour from the chalice, enough to feed all the hundreds in the hall.

Parzival ate the miraculous food along with the rest, but asked no question as to its origin. The meal over, the wounded king sighed deeply and left the hall. One by one the knights followed him and, without exception, looked back over their shoulders at Parzival as they departed, clearly disappointed. Parzival felt he had mortally offended his generous host, but could not imagine in what way.

Servants conducted him to a bedchamber. On the way he passed an open door and saw an ancient white-haired man tossing and turning on a golden bed as though deeply troubled.

The walls of his own bedchamber were lined with tapestries and, as he studied them, he saw the king he had just met in the great hall suffering a wound in the side from the very spear he had seen carried around the hall. Now curious almost beyond control, he decided that in the morning he would ask for an explanation of all the strange things he had witnessed at the castle.

However, in the morning he found himself alone in a deserted castle. No one, not even a servant, was to be found, and when he approached the drawbridge it lowered itself without human agency. As he rode out he heard a mighty voice call out from the tower above him: 'You are accursed – for you were chosen for a great work, and you have left it undone.'

Troubled, Parzival journeyed on and eventually came upon the woman he had helped by destroying the Red Knight. She revealed that she was his cousin and that the wounded king was his uncle. The castle he had visited was on Montsalvach. She told him of the curse that could only be lifted by the chosen one who asked the king the meaning of his never-healing wound. She accused him of failing in the great task set for him.

Horrified, Parzival set off at once to rectify his mistake, but the castle on Montsalvach had vanished. Year after year Parzival wandered the earth seeking the castle, seeking to complete his task. Many were the adventures he had on the way. He longed for the wife he had left behind, but he determined not to return to her until he had successfully completed his mission.

One day he met a man dragging a woman by a chain, torturing her most shamefully. He was shocked to learn that the woman was the first he had encountered, the one he had so innocently kissed. The man, her husband, was still angry that she had given the favour of her bracelet to a stranger. Parzival, ashamed that an incident and a favour that had meant so little to him had had such dire consequences, hastened to explain the whole affair and did not leave until the woman was released and the husband contrite.

Parzival's fame as a man engaged in noble deeds spread far and wide and he was recalled to Arthur's court where he was knighted by the king. There he stayed for some time, but could not settle. One day he left in search of the Grail castle once more. His friend, Sir Gawain, decided to follow him, but was side-tracked when he met and fell in love with a beautiful lady. It turned out she was the very one that King Amfortas, the Grail guardian, had loved and for whom he had abandoned his responsibilities. For her sake Sir Gawain risked his life many times, braving the enchanted castle of the wicked wizard Klingsor and challenging another of her enemies to mortal combat. On this occasion, the knight he challenged sent out a champion to fight his battle for him. Gawain and the champion fought long and hard; Gawain was on the verge of defeat when his sister pleaded for his life. The champion ceased his attack at once and, with vizors up, both were astonished at the identity of the other. The champion was none other than Parzival himself.

For a while Parzival returned to Arthur's court – but not for long. Month after month he rode out in the world, dealing justly and nobly with every situation that arose, but never forgetting his desperate determination to find Montsalvach again.

At last, exhausted and discouraged, he chanced upon a hermit's hut where he sought rest and shelter. The man took him in and nursed him back to health and strength. One night he told Parzival his own story. It seems he was the brother of King Amfortas, and had accompanied him on his ill-fated expedition. Afterwards, instead of returning to the Grail castle as his brother had, he renounced the world and became a hermit. He had watched the lands of the Grail King become a wasteland, for the king, his brother, had never fully grasped what he had done wrong, and therefore never fully repented. The hermit then told Parzival how his brother had nearly been healed when the Chosen One had appeared at the castle, and how deeply they all sorrowed that he had not done what he was supposed to have done – that is, ask the question that would set the king, and the land, on the path to redemption.

Then Parzival wept and confessed to his companion that he was the very one who had disappointed them all. It became clear they were uncle and nephew, when Parzival named his mother. Sadly, he learned from the hermit that she had died when he left her to ride out into the world in search of adventure. When Parzival left the hermit's hut he was much clearer as to who he was and why it was so important to find the Grail castle once more.

This time it was not long before he came to a steep and forbidding mountain blocking his way. Hand over hand, he climbed until at last he stood upon the summit. There before him towered the castle of the Grail.

This time when the Grail procession entered the hall, led as before by the beautiful granddaughter of Titurel, Repanse de Joie, Parzival prayed for guidance to do the right thing. He approached the wounded king and, leaning gently over him, enquired what ailed him and what was the meaning of the Grail. At once the king sprang to his feet and the hall rang with shouts of joy. The spell was lifted. The king was whole again.

Titurel, now a frail old man, approached Parzival and hailed him as the next Grail King. Cheer after cheer greeted the news, and great was the feasting and rejoicing. Titurel could now die in peace, and Amfortas live without pain.

Commentary

IN WOLFRAM VON ESCHENBACH's version the Grail is originally an emerald fallen from heaven, a stone. Some scholars compare it to the mysterious philosopher's stone the alchemists so desperately sought. For me the power of the image comes from the belief that the emerald was once part of a mighty archangel's crown, but through Lucifer's failure to measure up to his great calling, it has become an earthly object. As such it becomes a kind of mediator between heaven and earth, the upper and lower realms. It becomes the symbol of our human aspiration back towards the perfection we lost when we, with Lucifer, fell from grace.

That Lucifer's emerald became the cup used by Christ at the Last Supper, and again in which His blood was caught as he hung on the Cross, is also appropriate, for Christ Himself is a chalice containing eternal life; if we drink of it we too may partake of that great gift. As the Grail temple built on Montsalvach holds a perfect miniature of itself in which the sacred, meaningful, object is kept, so Christ the man is the true chalice, holding in his hand at the Last Supper a miniature of Himself, which he gives to the world as the means of salvation and redemption. Some versions make the link with the Eucharist even closer by describing a white dove (the symbol of the Holy Spirit), which descends from heaven every Good Friday to place a wafer in the chalice, representing renewal through the body and blood of Christ. The water comes direct from God the Father, via the Holy Spirit, to the Son, the Grail.

The stories of the Grail were written down during a period of tremendous fervent activity in Christendom. The Crusades were in full swing, the Knights Templars (1119–1312) powerful and active, Jerusalem a prize worth dying for (Saladin held it from 1171). There must have been an expectation on all levels among the rich nobles and the lowly peasants alike that the possession of Jerusalem, the Holy City, would bring great material and spiritual rewards. Perhaps the authors of the Grail legends were subliminally thinking 'Jerusalem' when they wrote 'Grail'.

The wounded king was first encountered by Parzival as a fisherman. Was not Christ a fisher of men's souls? And had not his cipher been, for centuries, the fish? Had he not been wounded on the Cross by the thrust of a lance, a wound that would not heal until human beings realized fully what they had done – until people truly and deeply questioned themselves? Had not his forerunner, the herald of his mission on earth, been John the Baptist whose head had been cut off and presented to Salome on a platter?

I find it significant that the healing of the wound comes from the question and not, as it did with the ancient Greek Sphinx, the answer. Why? Perhaps because Parzival is not fully worthy of his great calling, in spite of his purity, until he is fully aware of the issues facing him. Similarly the king, and the land, cannot be healed until Amfortas is fully aware of how he has failed the Grail and what it truly stands for. Perhaps there is no answer to the ultimate question, but a virile consciousness that there *is* a question is enough to carry us forward at this stage of our development as eternal beings. Contemplation of how he received his wound and *why* it would not heal leads the king to this awareness. But he cannot come to any conclusions by himself – he needs the spark of direct illumination to be lit for him by the chosen one of the Grail, as Christians believe they need the intervention of the Christ for their salvation.

Although the legend is richly endowed with Christian symbolism it has never been accepted by the Church as an official exposition of its teaching, perhaps because it also carries such very strong pagan connotations.

Each one of the major symbols in the legend can be traced to several different sources. The Christian emphasis on Christ as fisherman, the lance representing the thrust of the centurion's spear while Jesus is on the Cross, the severed head of John the Baptist, the Grail as the chalice of the Eucharist, etc., can just as easily be read from a pagan viewpoint. In ancient Celtic mythology, the salmon represents wisdom, so the Fisher King is the 'seeker of wisdom'. Pagan kings were often sacrificed for the healing of the land, and in the Grail stories the fertility of the land is frequently linked to the health of the king. The severed head was a particularly important and powerful cult object to the pagan Celts. They took the heads of enemies they respected in order to borrow the energy of that enemy (similar to the Christian belief that the relic of a saint carried his sanctity over to those who had access to it). All over Europe skulls and stone heads from Celtic times have been found, in many cases used in religious rites as oracles. The story of the great god-king Bran in Welsh and Irish mythology, whose severed head went on prophesying for eighty years until its guardians disobeyed instructions, is well known. The Knights Templars, who were a strong force in Europe and the Middle East at this time, were thought to include a severed head in their secret rites. The Grail itself, as cup or container, is highly reminiscent of the cauldron that features in many Celtic stories: the cauldron of Ceridwen that gives wisdom; the cauldron of Bran that renews life; the cauldron of plenty that feeds the multitudes.

The fact that the Grail procession itself is all female is more pagan than Christian. In ancient times, goddesses and priestesses were highly honoured. The beautiful, mysterious women who bear the Grail remind me of the queens of the King Arthur story who bear his body away into the mists of Avalon to await rebirth. The fact that the Grail bearer was a woman may have been accepted by the Cistercians (who would not have accepted a woman as priest) because, to them, she represents Sophia, the mystic wisdom at the heart of Mother Church – almost always represented by feminine metaphor and symbol – or Mary, the Christ bearer.

The landscape of the stories ranges from the Middle East, the Holy Land, through Spain, Germany, France and Britain. Many of the outlandish names and supernatural events were borrowed from the Saracens who, as followers of Mohammed, were mortal enemies of the followers of Christ, yet influenced the literature and deepest philosophies of Christendom. Wolfram von Eschenbach himself claimed that the story had come to him originally from a Provençal poet named Kyot, who himself had found it in 'heathen writing' in Toledo, a known centre for 'magicians' in Spain. Remember that the Moors were in Toledo from about AD 711 to 1085. Their influence was still strong there at the time Wolfram was writing.

One of the most effective features of legends in general is that the stories seem in so many ways to be fact that, when the supernatural events happen, we accept them without question within the powerful reality of the story. The Grail legend, for all its extraordinary magical, miraculous and obviously symbolic ideas and events, carries so many tantalizing geographical and historical hints that people throughout the ages have sought Montsalvach as though it were a real castle in a real land. To this day, in Glastonbury in Somerset, England, many are convinced that the well called the Chalice Well is where Joseph of Arimathea hid the Grail cup when he fled from his home country after the crucifixion and his long incarceration. Healings and miracles have happened from the water of that well because people have believed that the Grail itself had rested there once – if not still. In the Middle Ages there was a bowl known as the 'Sacro Catino' in Genoa which, for many centuries, was thought to be the Grail. It was translucent green, apparently carved out of a single emerald. It was brought to Genoa after the siege of Caesarea in 1101 and it remained a sacred object until Napoleon had it examined in Paris and found it to be glass, not emerald.

It is worth noting the tight inner consistency of the story of Parzival, the interweaving of relationships that form a solid background to the rich and sometimes confusing ramifications of the action. The fact that the saviour of the Grail King is a descendant of the first Grail guardian and also of the one who failed the Grail is important. It suggests a certain pattern or rhythm that manifests itself throughout the 'inner' history of each individual in particular and of the human race in general. First there is Eden, where the innocent rests in blissful harmony with the Divine Will. Then there is the Fall, and the rejection of the Divine Will. This is followed by the long, slow awakening through suffering to the meaning of the Divine Will and why it should be embraced. The redemption comes at the end through a mediator or saviour. By emphasizing the relationships between all the protagonists in this powerful cosmic drama, we are reminded that all the apparently disparate elements of existence are intimately linked, grow from each other and are dependent for their survival upon each other. Though the Grail seeker, the chosen one, meets many people on his journey and has many adventures, no encounter is haphazard or meaningless. Note that the Red Knight from whom he won his first set of weapons and armour had stolen a golden goblet (chalice) from King Arthur. This unimportant cup prefigures and counterpoints the important chalice of the Grail. The adventure in 'defence' of the first cup is gauche, unwitting and casual because Parzival is still so young and ignorant. Throughout the journey Parzival is changing from innocent and ignorant boy, through sorrowful and despairing manhood, to fully mature hero, aware at last of who he is and what he has to do. The woman Parzival kisses irresponsibly at the beginning of the journey, reappears near the end, paying heavily and unjustly for her brief involvement with him. He learns yet again that everything he does affects others. We have to take responsibility for everything we do, though what we do in ignorance and innocence may not carry as heavy a penalty as what we do in full awareness. The wound of Amfortas does not heal because he knew what he was doing when he deserted his duty to the Grail and let physical desire alone dictate his actions.

All through the realm of myth and legend we encounter spells that cannot be lifted except by some quirky, apparently irrational, action by another person. The prince must kiss the sleeping princess, the princess must kiss the frog, the young man must kiss the hideous hag before she will turn into a beautiful young woman . . . Parzival must ask what ails the wounded king (or, in some versions: 'Whom does the Grail serve?' – which is another way of making the king aware of why his wound won't heal). The other person, the healer, must care for the other before he/she can release him/her from the spell. The healing power of love is involved.

When Parzival first came to the great hall in the Grail castle he was a 'tourist' gazing around himself with idle curiosity, carefully avoiding any serious interaction with the people and the environment. When he returned after the long journey of awakening he was fully involved, he knew that the Fisher King was his uncle and that the lady who carried the Grail was his aunt. By birth, by divine choice, he was deeply committed. He bent over the king with a heart full of love, and spoke the words that would release him from his pain.

TWELFTH-CENTURY LADY'S COSTUME

7

The Death of Baldur

SCANDINAVIA

Origin

IN THE TENTH century Harald Harfager was acknowledged king of the whole of Norway. Those jarls and princes who did not accept such an overlord went to sea to conquer lands of their own. Rollo conquered Normandy and Brittany in France, Ingulf and Orleif settled in Iceland, others harassed the coasts of Britain and the islands of Shetland, the Faeroes and the Hebrides. Some say they even reached Greenland and the coast of North America. The sagas, the ancient stories of the exploits of gods and men and the whole range of beings that inhabited the wild landscape of the northern subconscious, were therefore carried across the world. Saemund the Wise (1056–1133) is thought to have compiled the *Elder Edda*, the first collection, and Bishop Snorri Sturlason (1178–1241) the later prose *Edda*. Both collections come to us from Iceland.

A FIGUREHEAD FROM A VIKING SHIP (BASED ON A FIGUREHEAD
IN THE BRITISH MUSEUM, LONDON)

The Story

TO ODIN AND FRIGGA, the All-Father and the All-Mother, were born twin sons, Baldur and Hodur. The first was as beautiful and pure as sunlight itself, the second was as dark as night and as blind.

Baldur lived with his flower-like wife, Nanna, under a silver roof held up by golden pillars and was the centre of joy in Asgard, the city of the Aesir, through many summers and winters. However, one day Odin noticed that his favourite son's cheeks were pale and his eyes dark.

'What ails you, my son?' he asked.

Baldur shook his head. 'Nothing, my lord,' he replied.

Odin would not let the matter rest. It emerged that Baldur was having bad dreams. When he awoke he could not remember what they were about, but they left him feeling anxious and fearful. Odin and Frigga themselves had lately been disturbed by feelings of foreboding and were now more convinced than ever that something bad was about to happen.

Odin set off at once to consult a famous prophetess, while Frigga took the precaution of extracting oaths from every animate and inanimate thing in the world that they would not harm Baldur. She neglected only one: the mistletoe that grew high on an oak at the gate of Valhalla.

The prophetess Odin consulted was in the Kingdom of the Dead, and when he approached her in disguise he noticed that Hel was preparing a great feast as though for an honoured guest. Odin asked for whom the feast was being prepared, and was told that it was for Baldur, the son of Odin, who would be slain by his brother Hodur very shortly. Odin asked who would avenge his death and was told that it would be done by Vali, a stepbrother. Then Odin asked in a deep and sorrowful voice: 'Who will refuse to weep at Baldur's death?'

But he received no reply, and with a heavy heart he turned for home.

Back among the living, Frigga comforted him by telling him how she had extracted oaths from all things not to harm Baldur and showed him how the other gods were throwing things at him to prove that nothing could harm him. Even spears accurately flung glanced aside harmlessly.

One day Frigga was visited by an old woman while she was spinning her golden thread.

'Why are the gods attacking Baldur?' the old woman enquired.

'They are not attacking, but playing,' Frigga replied with a smile. 'All things have sworn not to harm him.'

'All things?' the old woman asked.

'All things but the mistletoe that grows on the oak at the gate of Valhalla,' Frigga said lightly. 'But it is so small and weak I have no fear of it.'

The old woman moved off. It seemed it was Loki in disguise and he now had the information he required – for he of all the gods was the only one who hated Baldur.

He took the mistletoe from the oak, made a dart of its wood, and hardened it by magic spells. He then returned to where the gods were playing and suggested to blind Hodur that he would help him aim if he wanted to join in the game. Innocently, Hodur took the dart and with Loki guiding his hand, threw it straight and sure.

Horrified, the others watched Baldur fall.

Baldur, the Bright, was dead.

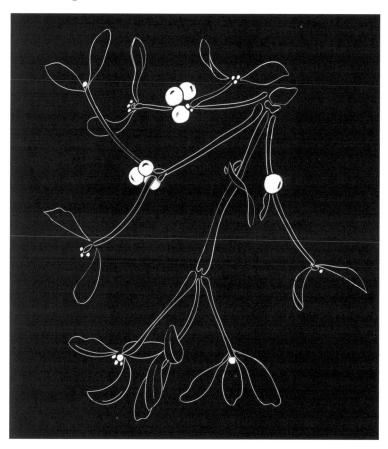

THE MISTLETOE THAT KILLED BALDUR

'Who will be the swiftest to reach the dread halls of death to plead with Hel for the return of Baldur?' cried Frigga.

'Hermod!' Many called out his name, for he was noted for the speed with which he could travel and was often used as messenger for the gods.

So Hermod was sent with Frigga's blessing on the eight-legged steed of Odin – swiftest of the gods on the swiftest of all steeds to ask a boon of Hel, the fell goddess of the dead, daughter of Loki.

Hermod journeyed over rough roads and through chasms where there were no roads, to the coldest, loneliest regions of the North. Nine long nights and nine long days Hermod rode on Sleipnir, Odin's horse, until he at last reached the tumultuous river Gioll, the boundary of Nifl-heim, the country of the dead. There he paused, contemplating the wild and rushing water and the slender bridge of smooth and slippery crystal, arched with gold, and suspended on a single hair. Beside it, on the other side, stood the grim skeletal figure of Modgud, the guard who demanded a toll of blood from everyone who crossed.

Hermod took a deep breath and ventured carefully forward. The crystal under his steed's hooves shook and swung alarmingly, but step by step he progressed, the violent and angry water far below seeming to reach up to grab him, its voice like the roar and scream of a thousand berserkers in full battle cry. Then he was over and Modgud, though she challenged him, was so astonished at the feat, and his explanation of why he was there, that she let him pass.

He entered the Ironwood, a dark and lifeless forest of dead trees with iron leaves. Thorns as sharp as spears and daggers tore at his flesh. Sleipnir whinnied with pain, but did not stop.

At last they reached the gate of Hel's kingdom, guarded by the vicious and slavering hound Garm – he whose howling in the end-days would draw all beings to the battlefield, the last battle, the end of all nine worlds.

Hermod reigned in his steed out of reach of the fell creature, dismounted briefly, and tightened the girth. Then, remounted, he drove Sleipnir forward with a great cry and leaped the gate, leaving Garm far below, powerless to halt them.

On the other side they could see nothing, for the darkness was deeper than the deepest night. Underfoot, Sleipnir's hooves slipped and slid on the ice, as they had on the crystal bridge. Around them they could hear the rolling and grinding of glaciers and the thundering of rivers too fast-flowing to freeze, carrying with them the swords of warriors turning over and over in the flood. Cautiously, Hermod inched forward, knowing that any step out of place could be his last. But care and persistence paid off and, finally, they reached Hel's great mansion. There, in the banquet-hall, Hermod found Baldur and Nanna seated together, for she had flung herself upon the body of her husband and died of grief, sharing his funeral pyre and the solemn sailing of his burning ship Ringhorn to the land of the dead.

All night Hermod spoke with Baldur, and in the morning pleaded with the goddess Hel for his release. She listened silently to his long and eloquent speech and agreed at last that she would release him if all things, animate and inanimate, without exception, would weep for him.

Encouraged, Hermod set off for home, taking with him the magic ring Odin had flung into Baldur's funeral pyre, to prove that he had indeed been to the realm of Hel and spoken with her and Baldur.

Rejoicing at the thought of Baldur returning, the Aesir sent messages around the nine worlds and everything, animate and inanimate, wept for Baldur – everything, that is, except Loki, who, in the guise of a bad-tempered giantess, refused to weep.

Baldur did not return until after the great end-battle and the conflagration that destroyed the worlds. Then, and only then, when the mighty Aesir were no more and the bright palaces of the gods were dust, Baldur and Hodur, his twin, left Hel's dark realms and together took part in the regeneration of the new world that rose from the ashes of the old.

A SHIP WITH VIKING WARRIORS (FROM A CARVING ON A
GOTLANDIC STONE)

CHERYL YAMBRACH ROSE ©

Commentary

ONE OF THE most frequent characters encountered in the realm of myth and legend is the 'trickster', someone who apparently does not obey the laws of the cosmic plan, who tempts and entices others to equal disobedience in an attempt to destroy the hero or the heroine. Such figures as Satan in the Garden of Eden, Loki in Asgard, Bricriu in Irish legend, the Raven and Coyote in Amerindian legend, the demon Kali in the Hindu legend of Nala and Damayanti, are of this type. So universally present are these forces, whether they be inside our own psyche or without, that one has to assume that they are an integral part of the cosmic plan after all. Maybe there can be no movement, no action, no furthering of plot and counterplot, no development or denouement – nothing – without their machinations. It is as though the pure and innocent spirit, living in harmony with its fellows and obeying to the letter the primeval commands of a good and noble deity, cannot evolve to a higher state if it is not challenged to defend its principles against a determined opposition. We sharpen a blade against a hard and resistant whetstone. We achieve spiritual strength by being tested to the limit.

The beginning of the end for the Aesir in Asgard was when Loki persuaded them to break an agreement with the builder of the great wall around Asgard. He further undermined the Golden Age of the gods by destroying Baldur who seems to have been 'the holder of the flame', the 'keeper of the light', the one uncorrupted and incorruptible being who kept the image of the ideal alive for them to follow.

It is interesting that Loki does not kill Baldur himself. His role is to cause others to do his dirty work for him. Hodur may be 'the keeper of the dark', but dark is not in itself evil. It is the other side of light without which light cannot manifest itself. It is rest in contrast to activity, sleep in contrast to waking, the cool of the shade under a tree in contrast to the heat of the sun, the open-eyed recognition of reality that helps us to distinguish between true love which accepts the beloved's faults, and sentimental love which remakes the beloved's image into something it is not. By himself Hodur would never destroy Baldur – for without light he himself ceases to exist. The fact that he is blind indicates he is an amoral force. He is not good or evil – he just *is*. After the great cataclysm it is necessary that both Hodur and Baldur, the twins, should emerge to regenerate the world. Without them both there is imbalance and instability, as Loki very well knew.

The mistletoe that kills Baldur is significant because mistletoe is traditionally associated with the forces of life, the white juice of the berries reminiscent of semen. Its roots never touch the ground and it grows high up in the sacred oak, so it is associated also with the fertility of the spirit uncontaminated by the dirt of the earth. It is ironic, therefore, that such a plant should be used to kill 'the keeper of light'. Does this indicate that anything – even the most pure and sacred object – can be used for evil purposes if the heart of the one who uses it is evil? Or does it indicate that the death of Baldur is part of the divine plan to destroy the world in order to prepare for the coming of a new and greater one? Must Baldur die as a sacred sacrifice (like Christ) so that a new, purer and truer life may be conceived and brought to birth?

In Norse mythology the number nine is important. There appear to be nine worlds created at the beginning of time. Odin hangs bleeding for nine days and nine nights on the world tree Yggdrasil to learn the secrets of the runes, the signs that not only help people to communicate across time, but can be used for divination and magic. Hermod travels nine days and nine nights before he reaches the crystal bridge at the edge of the country of death. In every culture the number three is extraordinarily potent and meaningful. We have the Celtic triple goddess, the Christian Trinity and Hegel's concept of the energy that drives the universe – thesis, antithesis, synthesis. We have the three Fates, the three primary gods of the Hindus: Brahma, Siva, Vishnu. Nine is three times three – thrice powerful – the number of completion and attainment.

The bridge joining two different realities cannot be of bricks and mortar. Between Asgard (the realm of the gods) and Midgard (the realm of human beings) there is a rainbow bridge. Between the realm of the living and the dead in Norse mythology is the crystal bridge suspended on a single hair. How often have we been shocked to realize how precariously our lives are suspended between life and death? How often have we said of a friend who is ill that 'his life hangs on a hair'? We miss death by a 'hair's-breadth' more often than we care to remember.

The bridge is crystal. Why crystal? Crystal is often, understandably, the symbol for purity of soul and luminosity of spirit. We see through crystal. Hermod can see exactly what his chances of crossing are and is not filled with false expectations. Its surface is glass-like, on which it is almost impossible to get a grip. One can imagine how carefully he and Sleipnir must step in order not to slip. It may be a bridge – but it is no easy crossing. Because he can see through it, he is at all times aware of the roaring torrent below him. In order to cross from one reality to another and hope to return the same way one must be fully conscious and cognizant of the danger of each and every step.

People who have had near-death experiences often describe it as a 'crossing', a journey from one place to another. They remember that the sound of blood roaring in their ears was like the roaring of a torrent; that the flashes of light, as they were absorbed into darkness, reminded them of crystal and gold. They remember the terror of falling and facing the unknown – even the feeling that they were being watched . . .

The descent into the Underworld to ask Death for the return of a loved one is a major theme in mythology, springing from our own yearning to retrieve those we have lost. That we cannot do this, in spite of all our efforts, is a sad fact of our existence. Orpheus went in search of Eurydice and won her right to return to earth, but lost it again when curiosity and anxiety made him look back over his shoulder to see if she was following him. Hermod wins the return of Baldur to earth – but there is one condition that must be fulfilled. It is almost fulfilled, but not quite. One dissenting voice undoes everything. The laws of life and death are stern but we must believe, for our own comfort, that it is within our power to retrieve our loved ones in some fashion, at some time. We cannot help hoping that if we had faith enough we might indeed be able to move mountains or bring back, as Christ did, Lazarus from the dead.

8

The Journey of Nala and Damayanti

INDIA

Origin

ONE OF THE greatest sagas in the world is the *Mahabharata* of India. It took shape in Sanskrit and was written down by Brahmanical compilers, possibly as early as 1000 BC, but over the centuries it accreted more and more stories until in its present form it is eight times longer than Homer's *Iliad* and *Odyssey* put together. It has been translated into innumerable languages.

It is rich in religious mythology and philosophy and is carried along by gripping tales relating to the Aryan tribal wars, notably the rivalry of two families, the Kauravas and the Pandavas.

The Story

WHEN THE GREAT and powerful raja Bhima announced that his peerless daughter, Damayanti, was of an age to be married, princes came from all over India to attend her *swayamvara*, the ceremony in which she would choose her husband. Among them was Nala, the raja of Nishadha. For years he and Damayanti had loved each other, although they had never met. A swan with wings flecked with gold and the voice of a human had carried messages between them.

On the way to the palace of Bhima Nala was intercepted by four devas: Indra, Lord of Heaven; Agni, Lord of fire; Varuna, Lord of water and Yama, Lord of the Dead, who

THE BRIDE DAMAYANTI

insisted that Nala should persuade the princess to choose her husband from one of the celestial beings. Nala pleaded to be released from the command, saying that he himself was hoping to win the young woman. But the celestial beings were adamant. Nala must deliver their message. They then transported him magically into the chamber of Damayanti without alerting the guards stationed at every door in the palace.

Nala and Damayanti looked at each other with passion, but Nala could not disobey the devas and, with a heavy heart, he told her what they had said. No matter how much she pledged her love to him he could not plead for himself at this time, but they agreed he should present himself with the other suitors and it would be up to Damayanti whether she chose him or not.

On the great day, nobleman after nobleman was presented to Damayanti, but she looked for no one but Nala. The devas, knowing what she intended to do, presented themselves in the guise of Nala and the young girl was faced with five men all identical to her beloved. In dismay, she fell to her knees and pleaded with them to reveal the man she so truly and deeply loved that she would renounce immortality for him. The immortals were so moved by this that they allowed her to distinguish between them. Celestial beings neither cast shadows, nor sweat. Their eyes do not blink and their feet do not touch the ground. Damayanti discovered Nala by the shadow he cast and the sweat on his brow.

For many years Nala and Damayanti lived happily, rich and honoured and blessed with a daughter and a son, unaware that Kali, a spirit of evil, was hovering over them, desiring Damayanti for himself. While they did everything expected of them by the gods he could not touch them, but one day Nala was careless and went to prayer with unwashed feet. Quick as a flash, Kali entered his body and set about his destruction.

Nala's brother challenged him to play dice and Nala accepted. They played hour after hour, day after day, and no matter how Damayanti and his friends pleaded with him to stop, he would not give up – though at each throw of the dice he lost more and more.

He lost his treasure, his palace and eventually his kingdom, but still he would not stop. Damayanti called her faithful charioteer to her side and instructed him to take their two children to her father's palace, for she could see that Nala would not stop until he had lost everything.

KALI

Stripped of everything at last, except a single loincloth, Nala was still eager for one more throw. His brother looked at Damayanti. 'Your wife is the most beautiful woman in the world,' he said. 'We will play for her.'

Though desperate, Nala turned away. As he and Damayanti walked through the gates of the city that had once been proud to call him lord, his brother issued a proclamation that anyone who gave them food or drink would be put to death.

Then began the wandering of Nala and Damayanti, destitute and outcast, eating wild fruit and roots where they could find them, sleeping on the hard ground under the stars. At one time Nala saw a flock of birds with gold-flecked wings and he flung his last remaining garment over them, thinking he would capture them to eat. But they flew off with his garment, laughing, for they had been sent by Kali to denude him of his last scrap of dignity. Shivering and naked, he faced the future – but Damayanti tore her own garment in two and shared it with him.

He tried to persuade her to return to her father where she would be comfortable and safe, but she refused to leave him. His own pride prevented him accompanying her to her father's palace because he was ashamed of how low he had fallen since his first appearance there in all his magnificent clothes, accompanied by richly attired retainers, elephants and horses, promising her a mighty kingdom.

They journeyed on, entering a dark and trackless forest. Wearily, Damayanti lay down and slept; Nala, watching over her, debated with himself whether he should leave her for, surely, when he was gone, she would return to her father's kingdom.

After many hesitations he walked away, and when Damayanti awoke she was alone. Miserably, she searched for him, weeping and calling his name. She knew in her heart that her husband would never have left her if he had been himself. She cried out with a loud voice and cursed whoever had influenced him to do the deeds for which he must surely be ashamed. In the darkness Kali winced and cowered – the curse driving into his heart like a stake.

Damayanti travelled on through the forest, always seeking her husband, with never a thought to turn back to her father's comfortable palace. A huge python coiled around her and began to squeeze the life out of her – but a huntsman heard her cries and rescued her. No sooner had he done so, however, than he cast lascivious eyes on her and she had to flee from him.

The trees rose huge and towering above her, and thorny creepers tore at her flesh. Sometimes she saw the gleam of tigers through the flickering leaves and heard the voices of approaching robbers. She became skilful at avoiding danger, her senses sharpened by adversity.

Damayanti came to a sacred mountain and pleaded with it to tell her where Nala was, but it was silent. She reached a sacred grove and saw the hearth fires of holy men. She told them her sorrowful tale and they told her that she would see her husband again, ruling in splendour over his people. She wept with joy at the words but, when she looked again, the holy men had disappeared and she wondered if it had all been only her imagination. She embraced an asoka tree, sacred to Shiva, and made her plea. But there was no reply.

She wandered on through dangerous and desolate regions.

One day she came upon a caravan of merchants and travellers on its way to Chedi. They took pity on the ragged woman and let her travel with them. At nightfall they camped by a beautiful lake, jewelled with lotus flowers, but in the night a herd of rutting wild elephants, scenting the tame elephants of the caravan, attacked and destroyed the camp. Damayanti managed to escape as tents and trees and merchandise were trampled to the ground. Many lost their lives that night and those that escaped blamed their bad luck on the stranger they had taken in. Once again, Damayanti had to flee for her life.

At the very nadir of despair she met a holy brahmin who took her to the city of Chedi. There she was taken in by the mother of the king as maid for her daughter.

Meanwhile, Nala's journey had been less eventful than Damayanti's. Not long after he left her in the forest he came upon a great fire, at the centre of which lay the King of Serpents crying out to him for help. It seemed a sage had cursed him and he was doomed to burn until Nala himself came to rescue him. Nala braved the flames and pulled him out. In gratitude, the King of Serpents told him that he would be restored to his wife and his kingdom – but first he must take ten steps forward. Nala obeyed, but before he reached the tenth step the serpent bit him. At once his body shrank in upon itself until he was no more than a misshapen dwarf. Horrified, Nala looked at the creature he had saved from the fire.

'Fear not,' the serpent said. 'This disguise will help you to pass unrecognized and my poison working in your body will torment the evil spirit that still rests there. Take this robe and, when you want to be visible as Nala again, throw it over your shoulders. But first go to the city of Ayodhya and offer your services as charioteer to Raja Rituparna. He will teach you many secrets about the throwing of dice, and you will teach him how to subdue horses.'

Nala did as he was told and lived for a long time at the court of Rituparna, but never day or night passed when he did not lament the loss of Damayanti and regret leaving her in the forest.

In the meantime, the raja Bhima had not ceased to send messengers out to look for his daughter. He found her at last through a holy brahmin who visited the city of Chedi and thought he recognized the pale handmaiden of the princess. He spoke to the queen mother and together they looked for the birthmark on the young woman's forehead, which would prove who she was. She was still beautiful, but so pale and wan that the brahmin could not be sure at first that it was she.

RAJA BHIMA DURING A MACE FIGHT

Among great rejoicing she was returned to her parents and her children, but still she mourned the loss of her husband and pleaded with her father not to rest until he too was found. Heralds and messengers travelled the country, but no sign of Nala was found.

One day a brahmin told Damayanti that he had encountered a dwarf at the court of Raja Rituparna who had reacted very strangely to the news that Damayanti had been found and returned to her father. He suspected he might know more about the whereabouts of Nala than he admitted.

With the connivance of her mother, Damayanti paid the brahmin well to return to the court of Raja Rituparna and make known there that the princess Damayanti was holding a second *swayamvara* to choose a new husband for herself. He suggested that if Raja Rituparna was interested he must get there within a day. This was almost impossible. But the raja spoke to his charioteer and Nala, in turmoil at the news, yoked four of the swiftest horses and swore to get to Vidarbha in time for the *swayamvara*.

Astonished at the skill of his charioteer, Rituparna wondered if the dwarf could indeed be the great Nala himself, famed throughout the land for his skill with horses. On the way they saw a tree laden with fruit and Rituparna bet his charioteer that he could guess the number of fruit on the branches exactly. When he did so, Nala asked for instruction on how such accuracy in the science of numbers could be achieved. Rituparna proceeded to instruct him in this in exchange for knowledge about the managing of horses.

As suddenly as he had entered, Kali left the body of Nala. Nala, seeing him, was about to curse him, when Kali pleaded for forgiveness.

'I have suffered agonies since the curse of Damayanti, and the poison of the King of Serpents! If you let me go now I swear that all those who love you will never have reason to fear me again.'

Nala let him go and sped on towards Vidarbha.

Raja Bhima was surprised at the arrival of Raja Rituparna, not knowing that his daughter had announced a *swayamvara*. Raja Rituparna, in his turn, was surprised not to see any other suitors for the matchless princess. Damayanti sent her handmaid to question the dwarf charioteer, knowing that no other charioteer in the country but Nala could have driven those horses at such a pace for that length of time.

She reported back that he had the powers of a god. He made fire spring from dry grass. He filled empty vessels with water. Flowers that had withered were revitalized by his touch.

Damayanti sent her two children to the kitchen. The charioteer embraced them with tears in his eyes, but still did not admit that he was Nala. Damayanti and the queen told Bhima that they were sure the charioteer was Nala, and he was summoned before the raja. There he broke down and he and Damayanti were reconciled. He told her about Kali's possession of his body and she admitted the *swayamvara* had been a ruse to get him to her side. All was forgiven. Nala then put on the robe from the King of Serpents and was restored to his own shape and size.

After the celebrations and rejoicing, Nala insisted on returning to his old kingdom. There he faced his usurping brother and offered to play him once last game of dice.

'Winner takes all – including Damayanti,' Nala said.

Smiling, the brother accepted.

But his smile soon faded when Nala won, and all his treasures and his kingdom were restored to him. He expected to be punished for the way he had treated Nala, but the king generously forgave him and set him up in his own city with his own revenues.

'For,' said Nala simply, 'you are my brother.'

Commentary

Like Shakespeare's tragic heroes, Hamlet, Macbeth, and Othello, Nala is a great and honourable man with a potential to be the perfect monarch but for one thing, the 'tragic flaw', which brings him down and for which he has to pay dearly. The journey towards his redemption, when he can become what he was meant to be, is long and hard, not only for himself but for his 'other self', his beloved Damayanti.

He is noted for his skills in taming and controlling horses. This, interpreted esoterically, suggests that he can control all the wild and dangerous impulses of his own nature. All but one – the impulse to gamble. But even this is under control until Kali enters his body. However, Kali could not have done so if he had not been careless about his duties to the gods.

The Hindu scriptures often refer to the three worlds: the Natural (the physical, material world we see about us on this earth); the Higher Supernatural; and the Lower Supernatural. In these stories, life appears to me very like a game of three-dimensional chess, played in all three worlds simultaneously. Moves are made by celestial beings from the Higher Supernatural world, and by demons from the Lower Supernatural world, but the mortal can still win if he learns quickly from his mistakes and keeps his wits about him.

The Hindu religious pantheon is complex and meaningful, but often bewildering to Westerners. The Supreme and Absolute Reality is Brahma and from this source, through the intermediary Ishvara, issue subsidiary forces and energies. Some of these are termed 'gods', such as Shiva, Vishnu and Devi; some are termed 'avatars' and these take on incarnation on earth in order to help the process of evolution towards release. Rama, Krishna (and Buddha) are such avatars. Other cosmic powers are known as devas – for instance, Indra, Agni, Varuna and Yama (as in the story of Nala and Damayanti). These dwell in a kind of paradise but come down to earth from time to time to interfere in the lives of men. The hierarchy continues downward with rishis, priests and various mythical creatures through which the gods can manifest themselves. The demons, lower yet, are constantly at war with the devas.

Kali is usually depicted as one of the great forces of the Hindu pantheon, the triple goddess, the powerful creator and destroyer, the Mother. Her worship is fearful and awesome, where blood sacrifice and terror are rife. She is the molten lava that destroys the forest and lays the foundation for the fertile soils on which future generations feed. She is the blood that pours out in agony at childbirth. She is the flood that kills and purifies. In this story the dark spirit that possessed the body of Nala and tried to bring about his downfall was an aspect of Kali rather than Kali herself. Nala has a flaw and cannot be the great man he is meant to be until he has mastered it. Kali, the creator/destroyer, the harsh task-mistress, the mother who beats her children in order to discipline them, sends her minion to teach him a lesson. Any activity that is uncontrolled and unskilled is dangerous. It is not until Nala has learned the science of numbers, the control of numbers, by exchanging with Raja Rituparna his own knowledge of how to control horses, that he is no longer in danger of being 'taken over' by an outside force or by his own wayward impulses, and he is then worthy to rule a kingdom.

Nala knows he should not leave Damayanti. He wavers back and forth. There are arguments for and against, and he allows himself to be swayed by the most expedient for him while telling himself he is doing it for her, illustrating yet again his lack of self-control at this stage of the journey.

Both Nala and Damayanti have experiences with monstrous snakes. Damayanti is almost killed by a python but is rescued by a hunter who in turn threatens her with dishonour. She breaks free, but her journey continues with almost unremitting hardship. Nala rescues the King of Serpents from death by fire and is rewarded. He may be turned into a misshapen dwarf but he is given a comfortable position in the court of the raja Rituparna.

Why should Damayanti suffer more than Nala when it was he whose fault it is that they are in this predicament? Is it because she refused to marry a celestial being? Is she being tested, like Job by Jehovah, to see if her love can withstand every misfortune? Is the burden of her journey to prove the constancy of her love for the mortal against all odds, while that of Nala is to learn control of himself?

The brahmins that feature a great many times in the story, seeking and eventually causing the two protagonists to be found, are of the highest Indian caste, the holy men, the wandering priests. Not fooled by illusion as easily as the rest of us, they notice Damayanti as serving girl and Nala as dwarf. They cannot change them back into their original condition – but they are part of the process. The final transformation has to come about voluntarily by the two concerned.

Having passed through every degradation, Nala assumes his kingship again only when he forgives and is forgiven. He is subsumed by love into his higher self and the 'Two' that never ceased to be 'One' in spite of everything, are recognizably 'One' again.

9

The Shaman's Celestial Journey

SURINAM

Origin

THIS STORY about the initiation of the Carib shamans of Surinam (formerly Dutch Guiana) in South America[1] is compiled from information in *Shamanism: Archaic Techniques of Ecstasy* by Mircea Eliade.

The Story

I SAY GOODBYE to my mother and father, my brothers and my sisters and all the friends of my youth, for I am going on a journey from which I will not return as the one who set off.

Six of us boys are chosen. I wonder if the others are as proud and as afraid as I. For twenty-four days and twenty-four nights we will be in training for the journey, isolated from the village, living with our Master in a hut set aside in the forest, covered with palm leaves. By day we will

HUT FOR THE TRAINING AND PREPARATION OF SHAMANS

work hard, tending the Master's tobacco fields, felling a sacred tree and carving the important alligator bench from its wood, whittling our magic staffs, and shaping the bells we will use if and when we are initiated shamans. By night we will be instructed on how to make the journey.

I am told there will be six girls under the supervision of an old woman who will tend to us, giving us tobacco juice, rubbing us down with red life-enhancing liquid.

Six days and six nights have passed. For three of these we have worked and fasted, for three we have rested. The alligator bench is ready, but so far none of us has watched for a vision on it. Each night, after we have danced and sung until we are exhausted, we sit on it listening to the Master's instruction. He is teaching us about the spirit world. If we cannot have conversations with spirits we cannot be shamans. We must know their names, their natures, the locations where they may be found, the ways they can help us, and the ways they can hinder us. We are taught about the great Grandfather Spirit, the Creator – but we will never see him or speak with him direct. Grandfather Vulture speaks for the great Grandfather Spirit.

Six more days and nights have gone by. We smoke, we chew tobacco leaves, we drink tobacco juice. We are instructed in everything about the animal kingdom. My hunger is tearing at my body. I cannot endure it. I crouch. I stalk my prey. I leap. I tear flesh. I am jaguar – and blood runs from my jaws.

I remember . . . What do I remember? I search . . . but cannot find my name.

What time has passed? I do not know. Much time is spent lying on the alligator bench waiting for visions. If they do not come, I will not be a shaman. What do I see? Movements in the shadows. They are there – the spirits – but they will not speak to me.

The Master stretches ropes taut across the hut at different levels. First we dance on the low ones. Then we go higher and higher. I am above the world. I hang from them by my fingers. I see the world dissolving and, standing before me in the air, a benevolent spirit. I cry out to him but he is already gone. I have had no conversation. Will I fail? Will I fail! My stomach is empty. My eyes are wild. There is roaring in my ears. I dance. I dance . . . Suddenly he is before me naked and ancient – Grandfather Vulture himself – showing me the spiral ladder my Master has told me about.

CHERYL YAMBRACH ROSE ©

'Come,' he says, 'come. It is time for your journey.'

I step on to the ladder. It feels like air, but holds me firm. I step. I step. I turn. I am climbing to the sky. I am journeying to the sky. I come upon a village. Everyone in it is as white as smoke. They ignore me. Beside a river I meet a beautiful woman who draws me into the water. I swim with her and, as we move together like one being, she teaches me spells. When I leave the water Grandfather Vulture leads me to the crossroads of Life and Death. There I must choose to go to the 'Land without Evening' or to the 'Land without Dawn'. As I approach one, the light dazzles me. As I approach the other, the darkness blinds me.

SOUTH AMERICAN VULTURE

Suddenly a searing pain shoots through my body and I find myself in the hut again, the Master bending over me and ants biting me.

'You must not go too far, too fast,' the Master says. 'It is not time to know these things yet.'

More time passes. I do not know how much. I am beyond hunger and thirst.

The Master puts me on a platform suspended from the ceiling of the hut and releases the cords he had twisted to hold it steady. It swings around and around. As I revolve I pass through the many celestial spheres of the universe. I see darkness and light run together like one thing and in that one thing I see the spirits dance. They speak to me. They cry out. Some enter my body and I scream and shake with the pain – wishing my Master would drive them out. I am torn apart. I lie bleeding. The spirits leave me and I am empty like a nutshell abandoned on the floor of the forest. But others come to me and lead me on and up. They fill me with their wisdom. I am full. I am whole. I can speak with spirits. I am a shaman!

Commentary

BEFORE WE CAN contemplate communicating with the spirit world, the other realms of being invisibly but powerfully surrounding us, we have to create a 'sacred space' in which we can work removed from the distractions of everyday life. A hut is built – roofed by palm leaves. The natural world is not forgotten, but it is ordered and controlled. Just so much of it is allowed into our consciousness that we may benefit from it, but not so much that it will distract us from our purpose. (Gothic cathedrals with their tall columns and fan vaulting also imitate forests.)

The novices cut down a tree and carve the alligator bench. They tend the tobacco fields. All this labour is so that they will appreciate fully the nature of what they are about to do and the 'tools' they will be using. Nothing must be given gratis; nothing must come too easy.

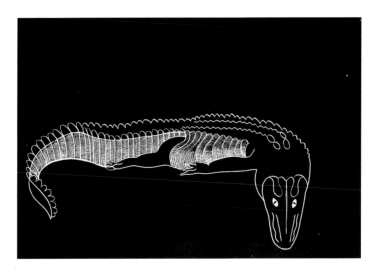

SOUTH AMERICAN ALLIGATOR

The bench on which they await visions is carved in the shape of an alligator. An alligator lurks invisibly in the mud and water waiting to pounce on its victim. It is powerful and dangerous like the spirit world, but a brave and skilful hunter may hunt it down and, when it is mastered, every part of it can be used.

The novices 'become' different animals. Experiencing their nature teaches them many things. The guide, a vulture, sits high on a tree or a cliff, watching, observing the minutest detail, waiting for opportunities . . . capable of flying immense distances.

The metaphor used for the ascent to the realms of the Higher Self is a spiral ladder. It is a spiral because the journey at this stage cannot be direct. Learning comes in cycles. When one cycle is complete, we may move up a notch only to find that we are dealing with the same wisdom coming round again – but in a more profound form. In the same way, we read a myth or legend or fairy story when we are children and notice only the adventure but, when we read the same tale at different times in our lives, we see more and more in it.

Then there is the beautiful woman who draws the novice under the water to learn deep, magical secrets. Water is symbolic of the 'source', the primeval ocean of consciousness. The woman is both the mother and the lover, from whose womb all life springs. Who, more than she, could possibly know the deepest secrets of life? The secrets of death are almost given – but not quite. Physical pain is used to bring the candidate back to earth before he goes too far and too fast for his own good.

At one time he is taken over by demon spirits – which is always a possibility when opening oneself to the spirit world. This is dangerous work and we must be aware at all times of both the dangers and the advantages.

In this journey the traveller does not go far from the hut outside his village, yet journeys through all the celestial spheres. Some would say that through isolation, sleep and food deprivation, drugs and fear, he is hallucinating; others would say that he has left the body and walked with spirits in the Otherworld. As fully initiated shaman he will be expected to guide and counsel his fellow villagers, heal the sick, prophesy the future – and he will be capable of doing just that! There is a great deal of well-documented evidence about the extraordinary psychic powers of shamans.

10

The Journey of Bran's Head

WALES

Origin

WHEN THE CELTIC tribes migrated from central Europe into the British Isles about 700 BC they brought with them their rich oral tradition of ancient myths and legends. In the long dark winters, when cattle-herding and warfare were difficult, bards told these tales around innumerable hearth fires. Centuries later, they were written down by Christian monks in monastic scriptoriums. In the telling and retelling, changes were often made to suit the individual story-teller, but the essence of the story survived and blazes through to us even today.

The best-known collection of Welsh tales from these early days is commonly known as *The Mabinogion*. Some fragments of these stories were known from the White Book of Rhydderch, *c.* 1325, but the earliest comprehensive collection was in the Red Book of Hergest, *c.* 1400. Both these quote from even earlier versions since lost. The Four Branches of the Mabinogion were not translated into English until Lady Charlotte Guest did so in 1849. I find her translation most valuable for its comprehensive and informative section of notes at the back. 'The Journey of Bran's Head' is drawn from a story entitled by Lady Guest 'Branwen, the Daughter of Llyr'.

The Story

OVER THE SEA came the long boats from Ireland, satin flags flying, warriors with shields upside down to show that this was a peaceful mission. Their king, Matholwch, was seeking the daughter of Llyr, the beautiful Branwen, to share his throne and his bed.

The High King of Britain, Bendigeidfran, Bran the Blessed, the giant son of Llyr, brother of Branwen, greeted them graciously.

'Two such kingdoms,' he said, 'should be at peace with one another. Come, sister, see what you think of this man, this king of Ireland.'

Branwen, dark hair bound with river pearls, gown of sapphire blue, as beautiful as the sea at dawn, stood behind the shoulder of her brother and looked at the man from across the sea. Matholwch of Ireland was a handsome man. Old women who are wiser than young ones might say he was too handsome. 'There is a prettiness about him,' one whispered to another. 'A weakness . . . He will be easily led.'

'No bad thing for the princess then,' was the reply, 'for she will be able to rule the land through him.'

The first shook her head. 'Not good,' she said.

Branwen was caught in the net of his smile and touched her brother on the arm.

Then began the feasting and the celebrations. A mighty auroch horn of mead was passed from king to king, and then to brother, noble, kinsman and companion.

Branwen's women took her away and decked her in jewels and flowers. When she returned she played the harp and sang, her voice as clear as the silver water that falls from mountain-top to secret forest pool, as joyful as a bird at dawn, as fine as the gold thread of a goldsmith . . . All listened, enraptured by the song of a young girl in love.

When she was finished Bran himself took the harp and played a stronger lay. He sang of peace between peoples and of Branwen as a golden bridge between two great lands.

But the mischief-maker, the shadow-spinner, the knave of darkness is never far away.

Bran had two half-brothers, Nissyen and Evnissyen: light and dark, the peace-maker and the strife-maker.

Evnissyen, returning from a hunting expedition, found that his half-sister was wed, and without his consent.

He said nothing to his kinsmen, but stormed out of the great hall on to the hillside where the Irish king's horses were peacefully grazing. There, in a savage rage, he pulled out his dagger and maimed them.

Bewildered by the insult of one brother and the praise of the other, Matholwch withdrew in haste to his ships. Branwen, weeping, was given no time to bid farewell to her family and friends, but was taken roughly, more hostage than bride.

Bran at once sent his brother Manawyddan and his best men to offer atonement. Each horse was to be replaced and the Irish king was to be given a staff of silver as tall as himself and a plate of gold as wide as his face. The companions of Matholwch persuaded him that the compensation was not enough.

'There is one more gift my brother Bran, High King of the Island of the Mighty, offers you in recompense,' Manawyddan said. He had been instructed to keep quiet about this last gift until there was no hope of peace without it.

'Give me the Prince Evnissyen's death,' Matholwch said coldly.

'That is not possible, my lord,' Manawyddan said quietly. 'The Prince Evnissyen is my brother's brother and the shedding of his blood cannot be undertaken honourably. But what say you to a cauldron into which the bodies of men who have been slain in battle on one day may be thrown, to emerge on the next ready to fight again?'

This gave Matholwch and his companions pause and they returned to the court of Bran to negotiate.

'I give you the cauldron', Bran said, 'to be held in trust, but never to be used. The warriors that emerge from the cauldron may kill, but they will

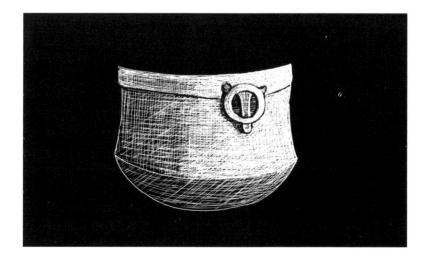

CELTIC CAULDRON

not know why they kill. They may walk, but they may not know where they walk. They are capable of neither thought, nor talk, and he who unleashes them on the world will rue the day. I give it to you only to show my trust in you and to prove that you may trust me.'

In thirteen ships the king of Ireland sailed back to his country with his queen at his side, and for a year there was peace and happiness as the people honoured the daughter of Llyr.

At the end of the year she gave birth to a young prince, and they called him Gwern, son of Matholwch.

By the end of the second year the king's companions began to murmur that the young queen was having too great an influence, not only on the king, but on the ruling of the land. They reminded the king frequently that her family had insulted him and were probably at this very moment laughing at him for allowing her so much power in his land. She was sent, on their advice, to work in the kitchens, and denied her husband's bed.

'Let the family of Llyr see', they said, 'that Matholwch does not forget an insult.'

Branwen's only friend during this difficult time was a starling who came for her kitchen scraps. Patiently she taught it to speak her name, and at the end of three years she sent it to her brothers with a message bound to its foot.

Buffeted by wind and storm, it fought its way across the Irish Sea and landed at last, bedraggled and out of breath, on the broad shoulder of Bran. Not at first realizing what it was he brushed it off impatiently but, as it fell, he noticed that it was a small bird near to death. Gently, he picked it up and cradled it in his hand. As it lay there he fancied he heard it speak his sister's name. And then he noticed a small piece of vellum tied to its foot. Carefully he unwound it and read there the story of his sister's plight.

Bran called a council and it was agreed that Branwen should be rescued. Seven princes under the command of Caradawc, his son, should remain to hold the kingdom safe, while the rest should follow Bran to Ireland.

Like a forest crossing the ocean, the masts of Bran's fleet put fear into the hearts of Matholwch and his men. The Irish king's companions at once advised him to retreat to the other side of a great river and destroy the bridge that spanned it. But Bran, coming to the river, laid his great bulk down across the water and became a bridge for his men to cross.

Matholwch, realizing he could not withstand such a force, sent messengers to sue for peace.

They offered that Gwern, Branwen's son, should immediately be given the throne of Ireland in recompense for what had been done to her. But Bran said the boy was too young to rule. The companions then advised Matholwch to offer Bran the kingdom to be held in trust for Branwen's son and, as a token of good will, a castle big enough to be comfortable for Bran to live in. Bran agreed to accept this offer for the sake of peace.

The castle was built and the great feast day arrived when Bran should take up residence as regent of Ireland. Evnissyen, ever suspicious, insisted on examining the building before his brother entered. He found leather bags hanging from all the columns of the feast hall.

'What do these contain?' he demanded.

'Meal,' he was told. 'Food for the new king.'

'Ah,' said Evnissyen, 'good meal, I hope,' and he squeezed the bag as though to test the meal. He smiled grimly as he felt a man's skull crack between his fingers. It was not until he had dealt with all the bags thus that he allowed Bran to enter the castle.

At the feast of celebration Branwen's son, Gwern, took his place at court for the first time and stood proudly before his kin. He bowed to each one, solemnly greeting them. But the boy, in his ignorance, bowed to a minor kinsman before Evnissyen; Evnissyen became angry and, when the prince finally reached his uncle, Evnissyen picked up the slight form and flung him bodily into the fire – shouting that he would be insulted by no spawn of Matholwch.

Screaming, Branwen would have leapt after her son had not Bran held her tight against his side, his shield over her, as every man reached for his weapons.

Then there was war again between the two lands.

As day by day the fighting grew fiercer, the companions of Matholwch reminded him of the cauldron and, although he knew that to use it might unleash forces he would not be able to control, the temptation to do so was too much for him. Every warrior that was slain was thrown in to rise again the next day to fight. Killing was all they knew and killing was all they did.

Bran's force could do nothing against them.

Then Evnissyen, seeing that his act was bringing about the destruction of his whole family and his entire nation, began to think how he could mend the situation.

One night, after the fiercest of the battles, he dressed himself in the blood-soaked clothes of a slain Irish warrior, and allowed himself to be

flung into the cauldron among the dead. Once inside, he stretched his limbs and strained every muscle in his body pushing against the side of the cauldron until, with an agonizing scream, he cracked the cauldron. He, with all the Irish warriors, fell into the fire and was consumed.

Only seven of Bran's mighty force survived this war, and only five of the Irish. The country was devastated: no crops grew; no birds sang . . .

Bran himself was wounded by a poisoned arrow and knew that his life was over. He called the seven to his side – Pryderi, Manawyddan, Gluneu Eil Tarn, Taliesin, Ynawe, Grudyen the son of Muryel, and Heilyn the son of Gwynn Hen – and commanded that they should cut off his head and bear it to Llandin, the sacred hill, the White Mound in Londinium, and bury it there, with its face towards Gaul.

'While it is buried there,' he said, 'no enemy will conquer the land. But first the journey must be as I say. Stay seven years in Harlech and listen to the singing of the birds of Rhiannon. I will speak with you as I did when I was alive, and all will be pleasant and comfortable between us. When it is time to leave you must stay four-score years at Gwales in Penvro and I will speak with you there. There will be a castle and in the great hall there will be three doors. Two you may open: but the third must be kept shut. If ever this door is opened my speech will cease and you must hurry to Londinium to bury my head. Mark well, and obey.'

Then the seven did as he bid them and set off for their homeland with Bran's head carried between them, Branwen mourning at their side.

But in their absence Bran's old kingdom had been taken by Caswallawn's sword and the seven princes he had left in charge were dead – even Caradawc his son was dead.

Branwen could face life no longer. She was buried on the Island of Anglesey.

On Harlech Rock the seven made their stay. Beneath them the silver waters of the bay lay quietly, half-ringed by shimmering, distant blue mountains. Bran's head was their companion. He spoke to them of war and of peace, and in all the speaking one thing was clear: no peace will hold in the world if it is not rooted in an understanding heart. He spoke to them of times when everything seemed lost, yet everything was gained. He spoke to them of times when everything seemed gained, yet everything was lost. He spoke to them of heroes who won all that they needed to win without shedding a drop of blood. He spoke to them of love and he spoke to them of hate and in all one thing was clear: he who hates destroys himself before he destroys his enemy, and he who loves gains more than he gives.

From across the silver sea three birds sang of life, and the life they sang of had no end and no beginning. 'The body is a seamless garment . . . and the individual soul is a bird of passage . . . but the spirit,' sang the birds, 'the spirit lives for ever . . . Yes! The spirit lives for ever . . . It cannot be seen, because it is the Eye that sees.'

The singing was the most beautiful that they had ever heard and it continued day and night without ceasing, though sometimes they were aware of it and sometimes they were not.

At the end of seven years they felt that no more time had passed than seven days and seven nights, yet they knew that it was time for the next stage of their journey.

Quietly they left the place and went to Gwales in Penvro. There they found a castle overlooking the ocean and there they settled with the head of Bran. In the spacious hall within this castle were three doors. Outside the castle four-score years went by, but, within, no time passed at all.

Bran's head spoke to them of the rise and fall of kingdoms and in all the speaking one thing was clear: no kingdom rose that did not fall. He spoke of lies and truth and flattery, of subterfuge and treachery, and told them that he who understood himself understood others; that he who did not fool himself could not be fooled by others; that the same eyes must be used to look both at self and foe.

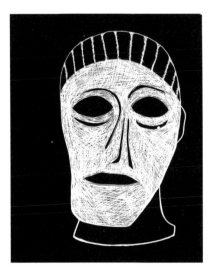

BRAN'S HEAD (BASED ON A CELTIC STONE CARVING)

They feasted on nightingales and saffron, on honey wine and parsley bread. They sang and spoke and rested, and in all things their mighty king was their cheerful companion . . . but one question he would not answer, and that was why they should not open the third door.

One suggested that it might be a vision of the future so disturbing that they would not be able to restrain themselves from rushing out to try to change it. Another, that it might be a vision of the Blessed Isles of the Dead so beautiful that they might want to leave this life at once to journey there . . . or so frightening they might fall into despair.

At last Heilyn, the son of Gwynn, could bear it no longer, and opened the third door. For a moment, after all their speculation, they could not believe that what they were seeing was no more than the ordinary world they had left behind. They saw farmers ploughing the land, they saw roads crowded with people hurrying to market; they saw trees bending in the wind . . . but most of all they saw the pains and sorrows of that world and remembered their great loss in the death of their High King.

Suddenly their castle seemed like a prison and they longed to walk on the roads among people again.

They looked at the head of Bran, and they could not believe that it had spoken to them. The flesh was beginning to slough off and the eyes were dead and glassy. Hastily, they wrapped it in a cloak and carried it as quickly as they could to Londinium where they buried it as Bran requested, beneath Llandin, the sacred mound.

By Arthur's time, Bran's head had lain for centuries beneath the Holy Hill, while pilgrims had come from far and wide to consult it as oracle and ask for healing. Many were the miracles that were reported from the place, and many a wise decision was made under its guidance. In his youth, Merlin himself sought teaching from the head, and was among those who journeyed every year at the winter solstice to celebrate Bran's victory over death.

The head became many things to many people: some murmured that Bran had been the first to bring Christianity to this land and that is was in Christ's power that his head still prophesied and healed. Others said that he had been an ancient god, denied by the Christians, yet still prophesying and healing in the tradition of the pagan religions. Whatever the form of their belief, the head still spoke to them, for it was speaking to the deep levels within the human heart where the true spirit abides.

Then from across the sea came the Germanic tribes – the Angles, the Saxons and the Jutes – sails billowing, warriors drumming on their shields.

In terror and despair many rushed to the shrine of Bran and demanded a magic thunderbolt . . . a host of avenging ravens . . .

Quietly and calmly, gazing across the centuries, Bran prophesied a nation which gained its strength not from the purity of its blood but from the strengths of many nations working together within it . . .

And then King Arthur rose and came to the White Mound, the Holy Hill gleaming with its white quartz covering.

'Bran,' he said, 'mighty king of old. The people turn to you, expecting you to provide a miracle to save us from the foe. They do nothing to protect themselves, but call on you, invoking your ancient magic, your legendary power. I am a warrior and I rely on my own strong arm to defend myself against my enemy.

'See,' he then declared to his distraught people, 'this old skull has no magic power to save you!'

He had the ancient head dug up.

'Throw it in the river,' he commanded, 'and let the tide take it where it will.'

Horrified, the people stood beside the river gazing at the spot where their holy relic, their powerful talisman, had entered the water. They expected some sign, some great portent . . . perhaps they thought Arthur would be struck down for his act of sacrilege. But nothing happened.

The water closed over its new burden as it had closed over all others.

THE CELTIC GOD CERNUNNOS (FROM THE GUNDERSTRUP CAULDRON)

Commentary

THIS IS A story of multiple journeys.

The Irish king Matholwch journeys over the sea to Wales to seek a bride. The bride Branwen journeys over the sea to Ireland to be with her husband. Her friend, the bird, journeys across the sea back to Wales bearing a message. Bran journeys over the sea to Ireland to free his sister. His head is carried back to Wales by boat and then on into southern Britain to London where it passes into the River Thames and out to sea. Up to this point the journeys have been across the surface of the sea. We live our lives with the great spiritual ocean of consciousness ever present, yet we never do more than skim its surface. When we enter it finally we are absorbed back into eternity. Because his people needed him, Bran's spirit hovered close to the earth-plane, teaching and prophesying. Each period of the journey of the head was necessary and significant. But when the people had come to rely too much on him, a man of action arose who forced them to learn self-reliance.

Bran has two half-brothers, a peace-maker and a war-maker — the two sides of the human psyche, of the lesser self. Bran represents the higher self — the presiding 'masculine' eternal principle. Branwen is Bran's sister — the presiding 'feminine' eternal principle, which is misunderstood, misrepresented and misused by the worldly. She is rescued by the faint chirping of a bird — the 'still small voice' of the spirit, taught to speak one word in the language that is unfamiliar to it, but which the world understands, and sent on the perilous journey through storm and tempest to draw Branwen's other half (her brother) to her side. Reunited — it looks as though the world will be at peace at last — but the lesser self finds it difficult to understand the higher self and sets about undoing all its good work at once.

In isolating the threads of this rich weave we notice Bran's transformation from honoured king to spiritual avatar and Branwen's transformation from princess to kitchen-maid, thence to honoured queen and tragic heroine whose story is sung by bards for generations as a warning and an inspiration. We notice the evil, selfish, proud Evnissyen (the little self) causing disorder and suffering where he can. We see him considering the result of his actions at last and transforming from cruel and selfish bully into unselfish hero, giving his life to undo the harm he has done. We see Matholwch the weak and handsome Irish king swayed by hearsay and gossip, understanding in the end that he must give up his sovereignty because he is not worthy of it.

Like all good tales the major theme is the conflict between good and evil, leading to guilt and redemption. There is no easy resolution. Bran dies — as Christ dies. He leaves behind one last instruction for his people. 'Do not open the third door,' says Bran's head. 'Do not eat of the Tree of Knowledge,' says Jehovah. Both instructions are disobeyed. Exile from Eden follows. It is meant to follow. It is part of the plan.

What about the three enigmatic doors? *The Mabinogion* itself does not disclose the nature of the first two, but it seems to me that if the third gave them such a shock when they opened it because it reminded them of the pain and sorrows of the 'ordinary' life they had left behind, then what they saw through the other two must have kept them from seeing these things. Because of the rarefied state of psychic excitement they must have been in to communicate so intensely with their dead leader they could not afford to be overwhelmed by mundane considerations. I suggest the first door would give them access to the past, the meaningful tradition of their ancestors. The second would give them access to the spirit world. The third must not be opened, for to do so would allow the distractions of the mundane world in again, and they would no longer be able to communicate with their dead leader.

These days the popularity of 'channelling', that is, the channelling of the voice of a long-dead master through a medium, is on the increase. People pay large sums of money to sit at the feet of someone who has this capability or to buy a book purporting to have been thus channelled. Believing, as I do, in eternal life and the very real presence of the spirit world around us, I do also believe that this channelling is possible, while retaining a healthy scepticism that not all that purports to come from a wise spirit from the other world is in fact just that. But one thing is clear, if one is to channel one must be in a heightened state of awareness and not lost in the hurly-burly of the everyday world. If one is to channel one must shut off certain parts of one's awareness, in order to concentrate on others.

It is interesting that the Templars, those powerful knights at the time of the Crusades who made their headquarters in the ruins of the great Temple in Jerusalem, were said to 'speak' to a stone head in the way Bran's followers spoke to his. This was one of the things held against them when their organization was finally toppled by the pope. In Scandinavian mythology the severed head of Mimir, the All-Wise, was kept by Odin for divination.

The White Mound in London, traditionally the burial place of Bran's head, is thought to be either the mound on which the Tower of London now stands, or that of St Paul's Cathedral. At the Tower of London ravens are kept to this day with their wings clipped because there is a superstition that London will fall when they leave. Ravens were the totem birds of Bran.

CELTIC TRADITIONAL SYMBOL

11

The Journey to the Fourth World

NORTH AMERICA

THIS STORY IS based on information in *The Book of the Hopi: The First Revelation of the Hopi's Historical and Religious World View of Life* by Frank Waters. Drawings and source material were recorded by Oswald White Bear Fredericks. This book is an invaluable compendium of Hopi knowledge and wisdom as given to a respected white author by elders of the Hopi tribe.

The Hopi themselves, after their many migrations, settled in the hot, dry, mesa lands of New Mexico, Arizona, Colorado and Utah. Their oldest settlement is at Oraibi. In their own minds they are the original inhabitants of America.

HOPI DESIGN

The Story

FIRST THERE WAS the Creator, Taiowa, and all that was existed in his thought.

Then he manifested a Great Being, Sótuknang, to carry out his plans.

From endless space Sótuknang formed nine universes. One for Taiowa, one for himself and seven for all that was to come. He made sure they were in harmony with each other as Taiowa instructed, and ensured that they had water and air.

Then Taiowa instructed him to create life on Tokpela, the first world, and Sótuknang created a helpmate for himself, Spider Woman. She took the dust of the first world, mixed it with the saliva from her mouth and moulded it into two beings, twins.

Opening their eyes they looked around and, in wonderment, asked who they were and why they were there. She told them they had been created to bring stability and order to the world. The one on her right was to travel far and wide, touching the substance of the world until it solidified. The other was to create sound until the whole world vibrated in harmony with the voice of Taiowa. Then they were established in their places, one at the South Pole and one at the North Pole, to keep the world spinning.

Then Spider Woman created the plants, animals, fishes and birds – singing with joy at the beauty of it all.

Taiowa looked at her creations and was pleased. 'Now it is time for a further creation,' he said, and Spider Woman mixed the dust with her saliva and created humankind in four colours: red, yellow, white and black. They looked around wondering who they were and why they were there. But they could not speak. Spider Woman, seeing this, called on Taiowa. He touched their lips and gave them speech to express their thoughts.

'Live and be happy in wisdom and harmony,' he told them. 'Respect the Creator who made you and one another.'

Spider Woman told them that the sun would remind them of Taiowa, their father, and the earth would remind them of their mother. These were their real parents and must never be forgotten.

The people lived in wisdom and harmony, regularly dancing and singing songs of praise to their father and their mother.

For a long time all was well.

Then came Lavaihoya, the Talker, who persuaded the animals to shun and fear people, and the people to forget their origins and turn against one another. A snake came to sow suspicion and dissent amongst them. It was not long before the people were warring against one another.

Sótuknang called upon Taiowa, and they agreed everything was going wrong with this first world and it should be destroyed.

'But there are some who still honour their Creator and live in harmony with one another,' Sótuknang said. So Taiowa suggested a plan. Those who were chosen to survive the destruction of the first world should be instructed to journey long and hard, following a cloud by day and a star by night, until they came at last to a giant ant-hill. There he placed his chosen ones with the ant people to be safe.

Then Sótuknang, who had created the first world on the instructions of Taiowa, destroyed it by fire. Great volcanoes opened up and poured burning lava over the land. The air was black with acrid smoke.

When it was over and had begun to cool he made the second world, Tokpa, putting water where there had been land and land where there had been water, so that when he called upon the chosen people to emerge at last there would be nothing to remind them of the landscapes they had once known.

The people spread out into this new world and multiplied. They lived in harmony with each other and with their true father and mother, but were never as close to the animals as they had been at the beginning of the first world.

Gradually they began to trade and barter between themselves and this led to inequalities as some people grew greedy and accumulated more than their fair share of material goods. Soon there were quarrels leading to wars. Most of them were so busy 'getting and spending' that they forgot to sing praises to their Creator.

HOPI TRADITIONAL DESIGN

Once again Sótuknang and Taiowa decided it was time to start again. Those who were still loyal to the great plan of the Creator were hidden deep in the earth among the ant people once again. This time, the twins who held the world steady at North Pole and South Pole were told to abandon their posts. Wildly, the earth spun off balance. Mountains crashed into seas. Seas overwhelmed lands. Ice that had been pent up at the Poles broke loose and covered the earth. Only when the second world was totally destroyed did Sótuknang allow the twins back to their posts.

The third world, Kuskurza, was born. Into it the chosen people emerged and, as before, multiplied. This time they built cities and lived close together, apart from the natural world.

As before all went well for a while until they began to use their inventiveness to harm and destroy one another. They created shield-like objects which could fly to the cities of their neighbours and rain down destruction on them, then return to base before their victims could realize what was happening. Some among them tried to warn them that Sótuknang would destroy this world as he had the other two if they strayed so far from the directives he had given them, but they would not listen.

And so the time came for the destruction of the third world. This time the chosen people did not retire to live among the ant people but Spider Woman cut down great reeds with hollow stems. They went into these so that when the great floods came to destroy their world they floated on the surface. No one knows how long they floated, but at last Spider Woman

unsealed the reeds and told them to emerge. They found themselves crowded on to a small island in a vast sea with no other land in sight.

'Where is the fourth world Sótuknang has created for us?' they asked.

But they could not see it. One by one they sent out birds to look for land, but all returned exhausted having found nowhere to rest.

Sótuknang told Spider Woman to instruct them to make boats and set out in search of the fourth world, following only the wisdom they would find within themselves. They set off, and at last they came to another rocky island. But it was not large enough so they travelled on towards the rising sun. Eventually they came to a big land, lush and green, but Spider Woman would not let them stay there.

'The journey is not yet over,' she said.

HOPI TRADITIONAL DESIGN

They crossed the land and came to the water on the other side. There they made rafts on which whole families could travel. They journeyed on until they came to another land, vast and fertile, and there they made camp, weary of travelling, longing to settle. Still Spider Woman drove them on. 'This is not the fourth world,' she said. 'You would soon fall into bad ways here, for the living would be too easy.'

The people continued their journey across this land, too, and when they came to the water on the other side, they made rafts again.

'I will leave you,' Spider Woman said. 'From now on you are on your own and must find your way to the fourth world guided only by your inner wisdom. But remember there is a way to communicate with the Great Spirit. When you were born there was a soft open place at the top of your skull, covered only by skin. It closed when you grew up, but it is still a door through which your spirit may pass to seek help.'

They thanked Spider Woman for all she had done and set off on their own across the great ocean. After a long, long time they came upon a great land and knew that they had at last found the fourth world. Joyfully, they approached it but found they could not land because steep and rocky cliffs barred their way. North and south they journeyed, until they were almost in despair of ever finding a landing place.

'Let us open the doors on the tops of our heads,' one suggested. And they rested quietly, allowing their spirits freedom to communicate with the Great Plan.

'There is a safe place to land,' someone cried, and there indeed was a sandy beach they had not noticed before.

'This is the fourth world, Tuwaqachi!' they cried.

Sótuknang stood before them and told them it would be up to them whether this world would be destroyed or not. 'It will not be easy to live here,' he warned them, 'but if you respect the plan of your Creator and each other, and keep the door of communication open between you and your guiding spirits, you should be all right.'

It is this world in which the people are still living. The story-songs of their migrations across it, and how they settled clan by clan in different parts of it, are still sung to this day.

Commentary

FROM THE JOYFUL moment of Taiowa's decision to implement the Great Plan, through his pleasure at its initial execution to his ultimate disappointment at humanity's destruction of it, we are reminded of the Book of Genesis in the Bible. Both traditions are tapping into an uncomfortable truth – if we do not live in harmony with the natural world, with each other and with the divinity who created us we will be destroyed. Whether we believe our world will be ended by a Creator being who orders it and then stands aside and watches us, or by ourselves, is almost immaterial. The consequences of misusing our world carry an inexorable logic of their own.

In the Hopi myth the people are seen evolving throughout the successive worlds. In the first they lived as one with nature. In the second they developed a measure of civilization in which they started to build houses and barter goods. In the third they built cities and developed sophisticated and horrific weapons.

HOPI WOMAN WEAVING A BASKET

After the destruction of the third world the people who had been saved did not just emerge, start living and multiplying as they had before. They had to make an arduous journey, at first guided by a supernatural being, but later on their own. If they did not learn to communicate with the Great Spirit directly, they would be lost. They were given more hardships than ever before so that they would learn to cherish and appreciate what they possessed.

In the fourth world more is expected of them than was in the first three worlds. They have a greater responsibility because they are now aware of the consequences of their actions.

Musing on the modes of destruction of the other worlds – fire, ice, water – I wonder if the next destruction, if and when it comes, might have something to do with air: air pollution, acid rain, poisonous gas . . . And the journey to the new world, if there is one, will be even longer and harder.

12

The Three Journeys of Ilya of Murom

RUSSIA

THIS STORY IS taken from *Russian Tales and Legends* retold by Charles Downing. Downing himself found it among the collections of '*bylini*' gathered by writers such as A. F. Gilferding, A. M. Asta Khova and M. Speranski. *Bylini* are the epic songs from old Russia, passed down orally through the generations until written down in the tenth and eleventh centuries. By the end of the sixteenth century they were no longer so popular. The stories are about heroic warriors, or '*bogatyrs*', who defended Holy Russia from the pagan hordes of Tartars, and defended the weak from marauding monsters and giants. There were two great cycles of stories, the one centred on Kiev including the stories about Ilya of Murom. The ones centred on Novgorod sang the praises of Prince Vladimir.

During the Communist regime the old icon painters of Russia were discouraged and many turned to the decoration of lacquer boxes, exquisitely portraying the stories of the ancient *bylini* instead of biblical subjects. In many cases, the deeply spiritual content of the stories was not so different from the essence of the icons. I have seen one illustrating the three journeys of Ilya of Murom that was reminiscent of an altar triptych.

TRADITIONAL CARVED DESIGN

RUSSIAN VILLAGE (BASED ON LACQUER-WARE DESIGNS)

The Story

THERE WAS ONCE a cripple in a village near the town of Murom. Neither his legs could walk nor his hands hold.

One day his parents were working in the fields when Ilya was visited by three strangers. When they asked to enter his house he called out to them that he could not open the door, for in thirty years he had not been able to move his legs or his hands.

'Nevertheless,' called the travellers, 'open the door to us, Ilya.'

Without a second thought, Ilya stood up and opened the door and greeted the men.

'We are hungry and thirsty,' they said, 'fetch us mead from the cellar, Ilya.'

He climbed down the steep steps to the cellar and fetched a brimming cup of mead. When they had drunk it, they told him to return to the cellar and fetch himself a cup of mead. This he did. When he had drained his cup he felt a strange, throbbing energy throughout his body.

The travellers smiled and asked him how he felt.

He looked at them in wonderment. 'I feel as though I could overturn the earth.'

'Go down to the cellars again, Ilya,' they said, 'and drink another cup of mead.'

This he did.

Again, they asked how he felt.

He sighed. 'My power has gone,' he said. 'I feel as weak as before.'

'Remember this,' the strangers said, 'when you are a great warrior, a mighty hero.'

He looked at them in astonishment.

'Go out, Ilya Ivanovich, and find yourself a worthy steed,' they said. 'Take the first foal you see – keep it confined in the stable and feed it the finest white meat for three months. Then for three months keep it in a garden. For three nights sprinkle it with dew. Then see if it can jump the highest hedge in the district.'

This he did, and thus found himself a mighty steed.

From this time on Ilya saw no more of the travellers, but to the astonishment of his parents and all the village he became a great hero and did many death-defying deeds, defending Holy Russia from the invading Tartars and from robbers and monsters and giants. The stories of his exploits were told around many a stove in the long, cold, winter nights, and all who heard about the three strangers and how Ilya had obtained his strength believed that they were certainly no ordinary travellers, but the Lord Christ and two of his Apostles.

When Ilya Ivanovich was an old man – as old as men get before they die – he came upon the crossing of three roads, and there read a sign written in gold on polished oak:

He who travels the first road shall be slain; he who travels the second road shall be married; and he who travels the third shall be rich.

Ilya shrugged. He rode his horse boldly down the first road, wondering how death would be delivered.

He had galloped for three hours when he came upon a hill on which stood a gleaming white palace. While he was staring at it, the doors opened and out poured a vast horde of evil-looking cut-throats and robbers waving their weapons above their heads and shouting insults at the hero.

Ilya Ivanovich stood his ground and waited for them.

'What do you want of me?' he shouted. 'I am an old man with neither pearls, nor gold, nor silver – but I can make your wives widows and your children fatherless.' He brandished his mighty sword. The robbers faltered and some would have liked to turn back.

'Cowards all!' their leader screamed. 'Forward! Drag him down! Cut off his head!'

The robbers advanced again.

Ilya laughed. 'You shall not take my horse whose mane is threaded with precious jewels, or my cloak of marten fur with 300 buttons of great value, for I have a bow and ten true arrows!'

But the robbers came, led by their wild-eyed captain.

Then Ilya stretched his bow and let fly an arrow at the earth ahead of them. So great was the impact of that shaft that the earth shook and clouds of dust rose to the sky. The robbers scattered in confusion but Ilya did not rest until he had slain every one.

Only then did he turn around and ride back the way he had come.

At the crossroads he scratched new words beneath the old.

Ilya of Murom rode this way and was not slain.

Then he turned to travel the second road. He did not pause for three hours. At the end of this time he came upon a white palace set among gardens of great beauty. While he was contemplating it, the door opened and out came a young woman.

'Noble knight,' she said, 'you look hungry and weary. Come – you may rest here and I will spread a feast for you.'

As she led him in she leaned upon his shoulder and kissed his hoary cheeks.

The old man ate from her table until he could eat no more.

'Come,' she said, 'I will show you where you may rest.'

She led him to her chamber where was a fine, soft bed. All the while she kissed him and twined her young limbs around his old.

'Lie down, knight,' she whispered, 'sleep with me and you will never desire another woman.'

'You are beautiful beyond words,' he sighed, 'and if I desired a woman now it would be you I desired. Lie first, dear maid, and I will lie atop you.'

And he pushed her on the bed ahead of him.

At once the bed gave way, the floor opened and she was deposited in a deep, dark dungeon among the others she had deceived.

Ilya took her golden keys and opened the dungeons to release all who had been trapped there. And then he rode back to the crossroads and scratched new words beneath the old.

Ilya of Murom travelled this road and did not marry.

He had galloped for three hours along the third road before he came upon a giant rock barring his way. He put his shoulder to it and pushed it aside with all his might. Beneath it he found priceless treasure, gleaming suddenly in the sunlight.

Quietly he loaded his horse and rode away to deliver it to the poor and homeless. With the last load he built a church with a shining golden dome and melodious bells.

Then he rode back to the crossroads and scratched new words beneath the old.

Ilya of Murom travelled this road and did not become rich.

TRADITIONAL FOLK PATTERN

Commentary

THE THREE TRAVELLERS who heal Ilya of his infirmity are reminiscent of the three strangers who came to visit Abraham outside his tent by the oaks of Mamre and who prophesied that his wife Sarah would bear a child though she had long passed child-bearing age.[1] Abraham's visitors were accepted as Jehovah himself and two of his angels, while Ilya's visitors by tradition were thought to be Christ Jesus and two of his Apostles. As with Abraham, the visit of these great supernatural beings sets Ilya on a course that marks him out significantly from his fellow men. He was crippled and helpless, but he was chosen to perform great deeds by the Son of God and given the strength to perform them. He is warned by the weakening effect of the second cup of mead that he can lose his strength as easily as he gained it if he is not careful.

The story of the crossroads and the three journeys demonstrates that no fate or doom is settled and inevitable. His miraculous recovery from his crippled state proves that what appears to be our destiny can be altered by the grace of God. His survival of the three journeys proves that by one's own actions one can alter what seems to be inevitable.

In the first journey Ilya does not fear death. He accepts it as the rightful culmination of his life. Because he does not fear it he is not frightened of his attackers. Calmly, he meets them and it is they who fall back, disconcerted by his courage and steadfastness. He looses his arrow. His nobility, his Christ-given strength, shakes the earth, making the bandits uncertain of their own convictions. The dust that flies up confuses them. When they have lost their communal, but single-minded, drive to attack and rob, they are easily defeated.

He rides back and it is clear the prophecy originally written on the signpost has no validity. One *can* resist and win against violent attack.

On the next journey he tackles the question of man's weakness faced by the powerful lusts of the flesh. The young woman offers him everything his body can desire: food, rest, sexual fulfilment – but he keeps his wits about him and questions why she is so eager to hurry him to her bed. Is this really love? She is treating him like a passive victim, and not a respected partner. He does not succumb to false love, and frees those who have.

Likewise, he resists the temptation of keeping the riches he finds (and indeed worked for, by pushing the immense boulder aside) for himself, and uses them for the good of others. Again the inevitability of the prophecy is questioned. He has defeated greed, as he has defeated fear and lust.

13

The Voyage of Maeldun

IRELAND

Origin

MOST OF THE ancient Irish tales are pre-Christian, brought by the Celts from their homelands in Europe when they invaded Britain *c.* 700 BC, only slowly changing emphasis and detail over the centuries as tribes settled in different places, and finally taking on the shape we know when they were written down by scholastic monks in the period from AD 700 to 1200. The potent mixture of eerie Celtic story in which magical and supernatural beings interact frequently with ordinary mortals, and fervent Christian missionary zeal, gives these ancient tales a compelling power.

The text of *Immram Curaig Maelduin Inso* (The Voyage of Maelduin's Boat) was probably written down as early as the eighth century, though later much was lost during the Norse invasions. Fragments of manuscript and a still lively oral tradition kept it alive until it appeared in *The Book of the Dun Cow c.* AD 1100. An early text in Old Irish consisted of a prose narrative with a poetic summary thought to be by the poet Aed Finn.

A CELT

The Story

MAELDUN WAS THE son of a warrior of Aran named Ailill, Edge-of-Battle. As a young man, hot-headed and hot-blooded after a battle, Ailill raped a nun. The nun bore a son, called his name Maeldun, and gave him secretly to be fostered by her friend the queen.

When he was grown, a young warrior who was jealous of Maeldun taunted him that he did not know who his true father and mother were. Maeldun questioned the queen and discovered the whereabouts of the nun who had given birth to him. After speaking with her he set off to find his father, taking with him three of his foster-brothers. He was welcomed warmly by Ailill's kin, but told that his father had been killed some years ago by plunderers from the island of Leix. It was made clear to him that he was now expected to avenge his father's death.

Maeldun consulted a druid and was advised to build a boat 'of skins wrapped threefold one over the other',[1] and that he must take no more than seventeen companions with him because no more than seventeen would return.

He chose his seventeen companions but, as they drew away from the shore, his three young foster-brothers swam after him and pleaded to be allowed to join the expedition. At first he protested, but later let them climb on board.

As they approached Leix they caught sight of the man who had killed Ailill, but before they could land a strong wind blew them away from the island. The storm raged for three days and three nights and when it was over they were far out to sea, with no idea where they were.

After a time they saw land and joyfully rowed towards it. But they found, to their horror, it was an island inhabited by giant ants the size of foals. The next island they came upon, after another three days and nights, was heavily forested and full of singing birds. There they rested a while and replenished their food supply by hunting the birds. The third island was inhabited by a great beast that pelted them with stones. The fourth alarmed them because they could see giant horses galloping and hear all the sounds of a multitude shouting as they raced, without being able to see a single person.

After a full week of sailing they came upon land once more, and found a house on the shore with a door through which the sea hurled salmon. The weary voyagers entered and found comfortable beds and food and drink laid ready – but no inhabitants. They rested and nourished themselves before they left.

After a further long voyage, hungry and desperately tired, they came upon an island of steep wooded cliffs. The trees hung so low over the water that Maeldun pulled off a branch, but they could find nowhere to land. After three days and three nights coasting around the island they found that three apples had grown on the branch and these three apples miraculously gave sufficient food for the whole crew for forty days.

Another island had a stone-walled enclosure in which an extraordinary beast was kept. This beast would run round and round in its enclosure and then from time to time stand still, turning its body round and round within its own skin. When it saw the voyagers it rushed at them, but they fled. It hurled stones after them and one pierced Maeldun's shield and stuck fast in the boat's keel.

From island to island they went, witnessing on one great horse-like beasts who 'continually tore pieces of flesh from each other's sides until the island ran with blood'.[2] On another they found trees loaded with golden apples which, during daylight hours, were shaken down and devoured by animals like 'fiery swine',[3] while at night birds flew down and feasted on the fruit. Maeldun and his men raided the trees during the night but had to hurry away because the earth was burning hot underfoot 'from the fiery swine sleeping in underground caverns'.[4]

CELTIC MYTHIC HORSE

CELTIC MYTHIC BOAR

On one island they saw a tower of chalk reaching to the clouds on top of which were white houses. They entered the largest and found it empty apart from 'a small cat playing on four stone pillars which were in the midst of the house, leaping from one to the other'.[5] On the wall hung three rows of treasure in gold and silver: brooches, neck-torques and swords. On the tables was laid a rich feast of roasted ox and wine. Maeldun asked the cat if this had been prepared for them. The cat glanced at him, but did not answer. They ate hungrily and then slept wearily in beds laid with soft and shining quilts. Next morning, seeing that the men coveted the treasure, Maeldun warned them to take nothing. But one of Maeldun's foster-brothers could not resist taking a golden torque. Suddenly the cat 'leapt through him like a fiery arrow'[6] and he disintegrated into ash. Carefully, Maeldun replaced the golden necklace and, sadly, he scattered the young man's ashes on the shore.

After several days of travelling they came upon an island that was divided by a bronze wall. On one side there were white sheep and on the other, black. They saw the shepherd who tended the flocks occasionally lifting out one of the black sheep and putting it down among the white, where it at once became white. Similarly, when he placed a white sheep among the black, the sheep became black. Maeldun flung a white, peeled twig into the area of black sheep and it at once became black. They then knew they, too, would change if they were to land. They sailed hastily on.

Further danger awaited them on an island where they could see fat cattle on the other side of a river, but when they tested the depth of the water with a spear the haft was instantly burned away.

Later they found a land where all the inhabitants were continually weeping and lamenting. As soon as the second foster-brother set foot on it, he too began to weep and wail. Two of his shipmates set out to bring him back, but the same fate overtook them. In the end, Maeldun's men managed to rescue the two who had gone to bring the foster-brother back but he, himself, would not be persuaded to return. And so the second of Maeldun's foster-brothers had to be left behind. When questioned by Maeldun, those who had been on the island had no explanation for their behaviour other than saying that when they were among all those despairing people, they felt despairing themselves.

One island they came upon was divided by four fences: gold, silver, brass and crystal. In one section were kings, in another queens. In one warriors, in another maidens.

Later, on another island, they found a fortress with a moat and a great bronze door. The only way to the door lay over a bridge of glass. Each time they attempted to cross the bridge they slid back to where they had started. At last they saw the door open and a maiden step out. She walked easily on the bridge of glass, and at the centre removed a panel and lowered her pail down into the water below. When she returned to the fortress they followed her, but she closed the door in their faces. They banged for admittance, but the metal rang with such a sweet melody, they fell down one by one in a deep sleep.

Three times this sequence of events happened, but on the fourth day she came to them in silver sandals, wearing a filmy silk smock with a white mantle over her shoulders, and a circlet of gold on her hair. She welcomed them, each man by his own name, and led them into the great house, ushering them to luxurious couches and serving them food and drink. Seeing how Maeldun gazed at her beauty, his men asked her if she would lie with him, but she did not give an answer. Three times they asked; finally she told them they would have her answer in the morning.

When the dawn came they found themselves back at sea, with no sign of land in any direction.

They were driven off the next island by thousands of birds shrieking, diving and swooping around them.

The eighteenth island had 'a golden rampart, and soft white soil like down'.[7] There they found a naked hermit with long and straggling hair. A fountain yielded alternately water, milk and wine. They spent three days and three nights with him; when they departed he prophesied that all but one of them would reach their homes again.

The air grew colder, the sea wilder. They passed an island almost lost in black smoke and heard 'the clanging of a tremendous smithy'.[8] It seemed to them a huge smith came to the shore and hurled chunks of red-hot iron after them. As it fell into the sea behind them, the water boiled and hissed.

After this they voyaged on until they encountered a sea as green and clear as glass. Through it they could see mountains and islands in every detail on the floor of pure gravel and sand. But, later, the sea seemed to become thin mist and they were deadly afraid it would not bear the weight of their boat. Beneath them they now saw warriors defending their cattle against monstrous beasts.

CELTIC MYTHIC BIRD

Fearfully they sailed on until they reached a rocky island on which crowds were gathered shouting at them and throwing large nuts.

Further on, they saw an arc of water like a rainbow above their heads; when they thrust their spears into it salmon fell like rain. They were so delighted with this that they speared more than they could eat and when they sailed away they left behind them hundreds of dead and rotting salmon.

Their wonder was aroused by a mighty silver column rising directly from the sea and reaching up to the sky. Around it was a net of silver through which they sailed. From above they heard a voice that none could understand. One of the men took a piece of the silver net, but Maeldun warned the others not to destroy such a great work. It was agreed they would offer the silver taken from the net on the high altar of Armagh when they returned home.

Further on they found an island on a tall pedestal but, in spite of the fact that they could see a door, they could find no way to open it.

At one time they came upon an island of beautiful women and each man lay with one, Maeldun with their queen. Time seemed to stop and they grew no older, but notwithstanding the pleasure they were experiencing they began to pine for home.

One day they set sail but the queen came to the shore and threw a ball of twine to Maeldun. He caught it and immediately it stuck to his hand, and they were drawn back to shore. Twice again the same thing happened and the men began to murmur that it was because Maeldun wanted to stay with the queen that he would not let go of the twine. The third time she threw the ball another man caught it and when he would not let it go, his shipmates chopped off his hand.

Thus they were free at last to sail away.

At their next harbourage they found red berries that 'yielded an intoxicating and slumbrous juice'.[9]

Then, after much sailing, they came upon a forested island where they were given shelter by a hermit. While they were there they saw an aged eagle fly down and land on the top of a hill, carrying in its beak a branch as big as an oak tree. At noon two younger eagles landed beside it and started to groom it with their beaks. In the evening they ate the berries the old eagle had carried on the branch. On the following day the old eagle

CELTIC MYTHIC BIRD

plunged into the nearby lake where the two younger ones continued to wash and groom him. On the third day he rose, shining and invigorated. The three eagles flew three times around the lake and then departed.

One of the men suggested they all plunge into the lake to renew themselves – but the others were afraid. The one who had suggested it did so and found that his eyes were clearer and his teeth stronger; throughout the rest of his life he was never ill or infirm.

On an island full of people laughing and playing incessantly, Maeldun's third and last foster-brother was lost. He was so enjoying the merriment the others could not persuade him to rejoin the ship.

They sailed on without him to an island surrounded by a circle of flame through which they caught a glimpse of a beautiful and happy people beyond their reach.

Further on they encountered an ancient hermit clad only in his long white hair, sitting on a bare rock in the middle of the ocean. He claimed to have once been a very rich man. He had set off to sea with his treasure but his boat had stopped dead and an angel had told him that if he wanted to progress he must throw all his treasure overboard. He threw everything away except a wooden bowl, and his boat drifted on until he came to this rock – where it sank. He had been there for seven years and all that time otters had fed him with salmon and his bowl had been filled every day miraculously with fresh water. He prophesied that Maeldun would soon encounter the man who had slain his father. 'Forgive him,' he said, 'for God has saved you from many perils, and yet you, too, are men deserving death.'

His prophecy proved to be correct and it was not long before Maeldun, recognizing a falcon familiar to him from his homeland, followed it and found himself in Ireland at last. On the island of Leix the travel-weary voyagers were bathed and given fresh garments.

There was now no talk of vengeance.

Commentary

IN ONE SENSE this story is a deeply symbolic account of the journey of the soul towards enlightenment, drawing on images from ancient pagan sources, while at the same time being a literal, though exaggerated and embellished, report of early Irish Christian voyaging.

The years AD 480 to 680 are often referred to as the 'Age of Saints' because of the numbers of holy monks at that time. When Europe was suffering the devastation of barbarian invasions and entering a period we call the Dark Ages, Irish monks were keeping religion, literature, art and music alive. The Irish monasteries were the vital storehouses from which Europe later drew its own cultural revival.

The journey, or '*immram*', was an important part of the holy man's life. He would feel the call and set off, often not knowing where he was going, knowing only that God would guide him to where he was meant to be.

St Columba of Iona (sixth century) listed three kinds of pilgrim. The first are those who leave their homeland in body, but not in soul, and therefore gain no merit for the journey (modern tourists?). The second are those who cannot leave in body because of circumstances, but journey in spirit nevertheless (the hermits?). The third are the true pilgrims who leave both in body and will. Maeldun falls perhaps into a fourth category – those who leave for the wrong reasons (in Maeldun's case for adherence to the ancient Celtic code of vengeance), but who get caught up unwittingly in a journey of spiritual transformation.

The journey of Maeldun is important to us today because we are all on a journey of self-discovery and subject to strange and puzzling experiences. We all seek our true origins and are easily swayed by advice from others until finally we learn to find our own way to the place where our higher selves have been waiting all the time. The weary traveller changes garments and freshens up, ready at last to know himself and to forgive whatever has been done to him. He is not the same as he was when he set off.

In the young Maeldun we have a man living a healthy, normal, but limited life in the ordinary physical world, jolted into noticing for the first time that he is not who he thought he was, and life is not as he believed it to be. A druid, a Celtic sage and priest, sends him off on his journey with instructions. The boat must have three skins (body, mind and spirit), and he must take no more than seventeen companions.

Numbers have a great esoteric significance in all myths. Seventeen is the number ten, plus the number seven. According to J. C. Cooper in *An Illustrated Encyclopaedia of Traditional Symbols* 'ten is the number of the cosmos; the paradigm of creation', and seven 'is the number of the universe, the macrocosm'.[10] Do we therefore have here a number suggesting *the whole* – the microcosm and the macrocosm together? By taking extraneous passengers, the ship of exploration is out of balance and cannot reach its destination. The setting off point is the *whole* unrecognized. The final destination is the *whole* recognized. In between there is fragmentation, imbalance, and danger of losing all.

Maeldun is given a glimpse of his father's murderer but cannot reach him because the boat is blown out to sea. Storm-tossed, it passes from island to island, each time apparently getting further from his goal. Yet in the end, as we see, nearer his *true* one.

The voyagers come to an island of birds. They kill them and eat them. Birds are often symbolic of the spirit. At this stage they are offered the opportunity of spiritual help, but they are unable to recognize it, and so kill the birds.

A monstrous beast pursues them with 'clawed feet like a hound',[11] and they narrowly escape. Maeldun's men are frightened, not knowing what they are doing, or where they are going. Even familiar creatures like ants and dogs take on a strange and menacing new life. Once embarked on the journey of the soul everything looks different, unfamiliar. We have to learn again to *see*.

The island on which they witness horses racing and hear a multitude of voices shouting – yet can see no one about – may represent their first unnerving inkling that there is an unseen world of spirits surrounding them.

In the house where the waves fling salmon through an open door they begin to find wisdom, for in Celtic mythology a salmon represents wisdom.

Later, when they are near to starving and are fed for forty days from three apples on one bough, we remember there are forty days in Lent, forty days when Christ was in the wilderness, forty days of rain before Noah's Flood. Forty is a number associated with trial, probation, initiation. Apples, however, signify life-giving energy in Celtic mythology. In this probationary time they are given spiritual sustenance. Three apples on one bough suggest the Trinity of Christianity, and the three goddesses of Celtic religion.

The voyagers sail on – having learned much – but not yet enough.

When they encounter the strange beast that runs continually round and round the island and simultaneously rotates itself within its own skin, we wonder if we should think about the rotation of the earth around the sun and on its own axis – or should we be looking to the turning round of the little self within the greater self? The image also suggests to me the continual facile and circular arguments of unworthy theologians and politicians within the outward, public image of the stability and respectability they project.

On another island they encounter beasts resembling horses that continually tear flesh from each other until the island runs with blood. Do these beasts represent the human race – continually warring, continually murdering, continually hating? They had begun to be enlightened with the salmon and the apples, but now lose heart because progress is not as swift and sure as they had begun to hope. They notice, perhaps objectively for the first time, the violence and cruelty of the world.

CELTIC MYTHIC FISH

Weary, hungry and thirsty, Maeldun arrives at a place full of trees loaded with golden apples – but the life-giving apples have to be plucked when the birds that represent spirit are about, not during the time when the swine that represent the burning desires of the flesh are most active.

They come upon a house, rest and are refreshed, but the foster-brother steals a torque and is destroyed. All men need rest and sustenance to live, but treasure is not necessary for survival. Gold and silver belong to Maeldun's old life as foster-son to a royal queen. It is significant that it is his foster-brother who has to be destroyed at this point because he represents that part of Maeldun that might still have clung to worldly riches.

They see an island divided down the middle with black sheep on one side and white on the other. The monk who inscribed the ancient story might well have associated the shepherd with Christ and the sheep with sinners and non-sinners – repentance enabling evil men to become good, and failing to resist temptation leading good men to become evil. Nothing is immutable. But Maeldun is unsettled by the thought of how easily one can be transformed from one thing into another and resists the possibility that he too could, and should, change.

Maeldun loses a second foster-brother on an island where all men are wailing and lamenting. The part of Maeldun's journeying soul that is prone to despair when others despair must be discarded.

When Maeldun's ship drifts away from the island that has four fences dividing kings, queens, warriors and maidens, we understand that they are beginning to leave behind the divisions and categories society imposes. They are confronted by a bridge of glass, representing the fragile bridge from ordinary to spiritual awareness, which they cannot cross with heavy, clumsy feet. The maiden tries to show them how it can be done with the help of holy water, but still they cannot enter the fort because they drift off to sleep too easily. It is only by her grace that they eventually enter and are given sustenance. Is she Mary, the Mother of God; Bridget, the Celtic triple goddess; Holy Mother Church; or Sophia, Wisdom?

They eat and rest and the men woo the maiden on behalf of Maeldun. She says she will give her answer the following morning – but when they awake they find themselves once again at sea with no sign of land. The outcome might well have been different if Maeldun had asked for her himself, fully conscious of who she was and why he wanted her. To achieve enlightenment and transformation we have to make the effort ourselves – no one else can do it for us.

An island of noisy, shouting birds repels them. Birds may be of the spirit but if spiritual matters are expressed in a meaningless cacophony of sound we should sail on.

At one point the voyagers are refreshed by a fountain that yields alternately water, wine and milk. According to J. C. Cooper the 'waters are the source of all potentialities in existence . . . the undifferentiated; the unmanifest; the first form of matter . . . birth . . .'[12] The way to the Otherworld is traditionally over water. Wine is 'the liquid of life; revelation . . . blood . . . vitality . . .'[13] Milk from the Mother Goddess 'is divine nourishment . . . used in initiation ceremonies as a symbol of rebirth'.[14] Do we have here wisdom-teaching that involves birth from the first chaos, the unmanifest (water); then life itself (wine); and finally rebirth into a higher spiritual life (milk)?

A giant smith hurls burning rocks at them and they flee. A smith refashions metal by fire. The voyagers are not yet ready for such radical transformation.

They come upon a sea like glass. The exquisite beauty of the pure spirit world is glimpsed momentarily in the Ocean of Consciousness, but the glimpse is soon over and fear of danger follows. Below the surface, as they travel on, they think they see a drowned island with warriors and animals. The impurities in their own minds and souls cloud and distort the beatific vision.

Faced by unlimited knowledge and wisdom, the voyagers catch too many salmon and have to waste most of their catch. Ingesting knowledge is like ingesting food – it is no good pushing more and more down your throat until you have digested the last lot. In addition, the rotting carcasses of discarded and unnecessary philosophies can poison the waters in which new seekers of wisdom come to fish.

They reach a great silver column, its summit lost in the sky, and the sea covered by a silver net. 'And they heard a voice from the summit of . . . the pillar, mighty, clear, and distinct. But they knew not the tongue it spake . . .'[15] This must surely be the voice of God – 'mighty, clear and distinct' – but as yet not understood by them. The image of the silver net flung over the whole of creation making it all of one piece – interrelated and interlinked – is magnificent. We, in our ignorance, take one piece of it and offer it to our God.

The door they cannot open in the high pedestal implies that they are travelling deeper into the realms of esoteric mystery and further from the world of monsters and physical violence. But opening the door into that higher chamber is still beyond them.

On an island of women they settle down like Jason on the island of Lemnos. Presumably this represents the temptation of marriage and sexual satisfaction that might hold them back from the completion of their rigorous spiritual journey. We must remember the story is being inscribed by a monk. Their souls know they must sail on, but their instinctual reaction on leaving is to take any excuse to return. Only serious sacrifice will free them.

Their next temptation is found on an island of intoxicating berries – that is, false visions, false revelations.

The vision they have later of the old eagle rejuvenated by plunging into a lake suggests the plunge into the primeval waters of baptism, the act without which rebirth is not possible. It flies off in triumph, but in spite of witnessing what has happened, only one of Maeldun's men has the courage to trust the vision and plunge into the lake himself. The others hold back – still suspicious of commitment and still not able to distinguish between false and genuine visions.

They lose the third foster-brother when he joins a company of people laughing and playing incessantly. No doubt it is as bad to laugh and play incessantly as it is to weep and wail incessantly. And it is certainly bad to be so easily influenced by others.

As they journey on they glimpse an island surrounded by flames. Through the flames they glimpse paradise. Regretfully, they realize they cannot yet pass through the agony of high spiritual experience in order to join the beautiful people they see there.

Maeldun is led back to the point from which he started by a bird, a falcon. He follows it because he recognizes it as one of the birds from his homeland. How often we find the teaching of our own community less than interesting and turn to other cultures in the hope of finding enlightenment. We flounder among images and experiences that are alien to us, only to find in the end that we return to our original starting point – led by something we had always known but never honoured before.

The voyage of Maeldun is not the only ancient Irish tale of a similar nature. Perhaps the most famous of all is the *Navigatio Sancti Brendani Abbatis*, the story of the journey of St Brendan. Many manuscripts of this are still extant, each slightly different from the rest, but in essence the same. It is believed St Brendan himself lived *c.* AD 489–570 and that the first known manuscript may have been inscribed *c.* AD 800.

In the twentieth century Tim Severin reconstructed a boat of the type that would have been used by St Brendan and followed his route, using clues from the story. St Brendan's original boat arrived at last on the coast of Newfoundland, Canada, earlier than any known European reference to the New World.

I have dealt with the Maeldun voyage almost exclusively as a mythic journey through the inner realms of the human psyche, and the Brendan voyage may be interpreted in the same way, and has been frequently. However, Tim Severin has proved that these journeys could also have been, quite literally, real voyages on a real ocean.

Severin set sail in May 1976 for a 3000-mile (4800-km) journey in a boat constructed exactly as the legend says Brendan's boat was constructed: of ox-hide heavily greased with fat. The story of that extraordinary and courageous journey is recorded in the book *The Brendan Voyage* which, throughout, makes connections between apparently mythic places in the ancient saga and real places on the northern Atlantic route to America.

Severin encountered storms and gales that blew his little boat off course just as Maeldun and Brendan had, but found that the boat of wood and skin rode the waves well – in some cases better than a modern boat. Severin's crew experienced mists and fogs that came from nowhere and obscured everything, giving the impression that they had left the known world and entered the mysterious unknown. Severin saw thousands upon thousands of sea birds, pouring out from the cliffs of Mykines 'in droves, in squadron after squadron, wheeling and turning, and swooping and dipping . . .'[16]

From the Faeroes Severin followed the Maeldun/Brendan route to Iceland, encountering whales on the way when they were becalmed. The great, gentle creatures were evidently fascinated by the boat and circled slowly. In the Brendan tale, there is mention of a sleeping whale on which they land, mistaking it for an island. Sharks, killer whales and sea-lions might well furnish the imagination with monsters. A huge bull sea-lion, with its loose folds of skin, might well have suggested the monster that revolved within its own skin.

Severin identified volcanic Iceland with the Island of Smiths where lumps of burning rock might well have been hurled into the sea during an eruption. Sailing towards Greenland, Severin describes the Arctic mirage where 'the high-altitude Greenland glaciers supply a bright source of reflected light . . . the result is to change the optical properties of the air so that it bends the light like a giant lens. Objects far beyond the normal horizon now appear within view, floating above the horizon, and sometimes turned upside down and stacked, one image above the other.'[17] Could such an optical phenomenon have given rise to the image of the ocean as clear as glass through which mountains and forests appeared? No wonder the crew felt they were travelling through some strange Otherworld. Presumably Maeldun and Brendan must also have witnessed the northern lights.

Off the coast of Greenland Severin encountered icebergs 'sometimes one hundred feet high and more'[18] shimmering and dazzling. Is this not a possible explanation of Maeldun's gigantic silver column reaching to the sky . . . the creak and roar of the icebergs and loose pieces of ice grinding against each other furnishing that mysterious voice of God – heard but not understood? Severin's description of the loose, drifting pieces of ice covering the sea from horizon to horizon might well have been Maeldun's silver net.

In ancient Irish myth and art images flow through each other from the 'real' and the 'imaginative' realms until there is no separating them, both enriched by the vitality of the other. The mythic journey illuminates our own journey through life, and our own life illuminates the mythic journey.

14

The Journey to the Dragon Emperor's Palace
VIETNAM

> ### *Origin*

I FOUND THIS story in an anthology of Vietnamese legends retold by the Zen Master, poet and peace activist, Thich Nhat Hanh. The book is called *A Taste of Earth and Other Legends of Vietnam*.

Vietnam, of all the countries in Southeast Asia, was influenced most by the Chinese. In 214 BC the emperor of China sent forces into Vietnam and a long period of Chinese occupation ensued. In 111 BC Northern Vietnam was under direct Chinese rule and it was not until the collapse of the Tang dynasty in China *c.* AD 906 that Vietnam was given its independence.

One of the Vietnamese legends tells of Lac Long Quan, the Dragon Emperor, who came from the sea in ancient times and gave the Vietnamese people the knowledge necessary for civilization. When he returned to the sea he told them he could be called upon any time they were in serious trouble. At one time, when the country was invaded by the Chinese, the people called on Lac Long Quan for help. He rose from the sea, drove out the invader, and captured his wife Au Co. Au Co stayed in Vietnam and gave birth to the first native rulers of Vietnam.

The following story suggests a time when Au Co has shed her mortal persona and has become assimilated into the pantheon of local gods and goddesses.

A DRAGON IN THE OCEAN (BASED ON VIETNAMESE POTTERY)

The Story

THE COUNTRY WAS in the throes of a terrible drought, rivers and streams drying out, plants withering, people in despair. The goddess Au Co, seeing her children suffering, descended from the mountains to sit beneath a 4000-year-old tree in the village of Hac Trang to give counsel. A young man, Hung, was chosen to seek out the Dragon Emperor in his palace under the sea and persuade him to give rain. But Hung must not go alone, she said. He must choose a young woman to go with him. Au Co would give him no instructions on how to reach the palace, but provided him with a jadestone which she said would be of help to him.

Hung decided to take his friend Mi with him and found to his surprise that when he approached her house she already knew of his mission and was waiting to set off. It seems she had found a tiny pink fish in the shallow muddy water of a half-dried-out stream and, when she had rescued it, the fish had grown alarmingly until it was almost too heavy to carry. It told her it was the daughter of the Dragon Emperor and pleaded to be returned to the ocean. When Mi had delivered her safely she spoke again, seeming to know that Mi was about to go on this journey to her father's sea palace with Hung, and offering her help. The sea princess taught the young girl a sacred mantra which, when repeated, would frighten off any monsters that threatened harm to them. She also advised them to take a vessel of pure, fresh water to the Dragon Emperor, for without it he could not make rain.

Mi taught Hung the mantra and they set off on their difficult journey, travelling, as the princess had suggested, directly towards the sunrise. They located the dry well the princess had told Mi about, lowered themselves into it, and found a path at the bottom which led them to a cave deep underground, hung with crystal stalactites dripping fresh water from which they filled a gourd.

They then followed the path to the east, hoping to reach the shores of the ocean, but after a while the path gave way to tumbled and jagged rocks and they could scarcely find their way. A smell – and a sound – made them pause and look around anxiously. Protruding from fissures were human bones. They tried to hurry, but the terrain was against them. A hideous and monstrous being rose before them with a fisherman, still alive, hanging from its mouth. Terrified as they were, the two remembered the mantra and chanted it as loud as they could while Hung tried to do battle. As they reached the last line the creature dropped the fisherman and retreated to its lair.

The fisherman was sorely wounded but still breathing. Mi had been given a vial of special medicine by her mother when she left home and this she now used on the monster's victim. When he was sufficiently recovered they left him and hurried on.

At last they came to the Eastern Sea. There, on the shore, with the great orb of orange light lifting above the horizon, Hung held up the jadestone above his head. At once the sea parted, revealing a path of pure white sand. Hand in hand, the two young people stepped on to the path and walked into the ocean. When the water at last closed over their heads a bubble of air stayed with them so that they did not drown, and the light from the jade lit their way. After many hours, or perhaps days, for there was no marking of time in this strange world, they were so weary they could not go on. Mi remembered the vial of medicine her mother had given her, the medicine that had been handed down from mother to daughter for generations, having first been given to them by Au Co, the Great Mother herself. The scent of mountain herbs was strong as she opened the vial and the wonderful elixir soon revived them. They continued to follow the path of pure sand, but after a while found that they had lost it. They looked around in despair – having come so far, yet not knowing how much further they still had to go.

A small pink fish swam up to them and Mi knew it was the Dragon Emperor's daughter she had helped back to the sea. Joyfully, they followed her until they came to the palace, gleaming and sparkling before them. Through coral and pearl and sea-roses they wandered until they reached a great gate guarded by fearsome creatures. But the princess led them through this one and several others. At last she stopped and pointed the way.

'You must continue on your own,' she said. 'Through that courtyard you will see three portals. Pass through them and through the wide courtyard on the other side in which my father's most treasured plants grow. Then you will enter the palace and meet the Dragon Emperor himself. I wish you well.'

Mi and Hung turned to thank her, but the fish was gone. In its place stood a tall and beautiful girl already moving away from them. They stepped forward, crossed the courtyard, passed through the portals and stood for a moment dazzled by the exquisite sea flowers lapping against the walls of the palace.

Without being challenged they entered the Emperor's Great Hall and stood before a huge, empty jade throne. There was no one in sight. Nervously, Hung stepped forward and addressed the throne, speaking with great feeling about the plight of the people in his country where no

rain had fallen for a long, long time. Mi joined him, singing a prayer for help. They cast their eyes up at the tall columns that stood around them but they could not see the ceiling of the hall because it was lost in mist. When they looked back the Dragon Emperor was seated on his throne, his expression thoughtful.

'You have my jadestone,' he said, 'the one I gave to Au Co.'

'Yes,' Hung whispered. 'She gave it to me under the 4000-year-old tree in my village.' And then he told the Dragon Emperor the whole story of their journey.

The mighty being listened quietly and then beckoned them to follow him. He called his daughter, and together they took the two mortals to the place of clouds where Hung produced his gourd of fresh water.

On the land above the ocean the people ran out of their houses crying out aloud with joy. Clouds billowed over the landscape and heavy drops began to hit the dust.

'It is rain,' they cried. 'Hung and Mi must have reached the Dragon Emperor!'

Meanwhile, Hung and Mi were on their way home. The Emperor, disguised as an ordinary fisherman in a fishing boat, was rowing them back to shore.

The water stirred and boiled as the monster Hung and Mi had frightened off with the sacred mantra rose to the surface. The Emperor picked up his daughter and flung her into its ghastly mouth. Mi and Hung shrieked and tried to pull her back, but she had turned into a ball of fire and the monster was screaming in agony. Then the Emperor brought out a mighty sword and slew the creature.

The rejoicing of the villagers knew no bounds – not only were the fields green again, but they were rid of the monster that had been tormenting them for years. The Dragon Emperor and his daughter were among them and the drums proclaimed it. Everyone, old and young, danced and sang.

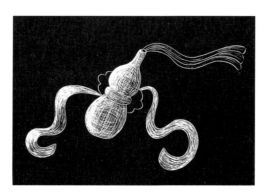

A GOURD FOR CARRYING FRESH WATER

Commentary

THIS ANCIENT TRADITIONAL tale is so similar to so many others from around the world that one is tempted to believe that all cultures were then in constant communication with one another as they are today. But its similarity is due rather to the similarity of experience the world over.

We all know of the drought when crops fail and people starve. We all know of the drought that besets the psyche when the 'waters' of spiritual enlightenment and renewal dry up, when we are no longer nourished by wisdom, but lost in the wasteland of petty material concerns.

Au Co, the Mother of the Earth, concerned for her children, comes down to give advice. Note that she does not tell them the way to the Dragon Emperor's palace because they must use their own initiative to find it. She does, however, give them a jadestone, a talisman, which is a gift from the Dragon Emperor himself. When they set off on this journey they must already have belief in the Emperor and carry with them the promise of his grace. Jade stands for the heavenly principle – the most sublime stone in existence.

Au Co lives in the mountains, like the Greek gods on Mount Olympus, for mountains are a universal symbol of the unattainable heights to which the human spirit aspires. The huge and ancient tree under which she meets the villagers has roots that go deep into the earth and branches that reach to the sky. It is the link between heaven and earth. It is a tree made sacred by millennia of worship and tradition, a tree that shelters the people from the scorching of the sun, and gives them a sense of continuity and stability. Anyone who has sat silently beneath a great old tree in the heat of the day may well have experienced a sense of communication with eternity.

Hung is chosen, but he must not go alone. A male and female must go together because this is a story about fertility – the fertility of the earth, the fertility of the human spirit. Both masculine and feminine principles are needed for a successful outcome.

Mi is not a passive follower. She brings vital knowledge to the journey. Au Co has given Hung the jadestone as a sign of grace. Mi obtains the knowledge that will help them on their way by a positive act of kindness. She rescues the little fish, not knowing that it is the Emperor's daughter.

The fact that they find fresh water dripping in a cave when they thought there was no fresh water to be found indicates that there is always some nourishment for the spirit if only we look hard and deep enough for it. Note they do not defeat the monster of doubt and despair that threatens to devour them by physical means, but by the chanting of a sacred mantra – some deep spiritual truth they have learned in times of calm to be used in times of stress. A mantra is a form of sacred chant, common to many Eastern religions, which corresponds to the vibratory pattern of creation. Mantras are believed, since ancient times in the East, and in the West, to have supernatural and magical properties.

Hung and Mi perform another kind deed – they rescue and heal the fisherman. Those who have the strength of inner conviction may help those who have lost theirs.

They reach the great primeval ocean from which, in almost all cultures, life originally sprang and to which all must return. It is the ocean of consciousness in which we are all one. It is here the talisman of jade manifests its power. It parts the waves and allows the two mortals to enter the ocean and travel safely to the depths where the great Dragon Emperor has his palace.

At first all is well – the path is clear – but then they lose it. We know this so well. How many times have we started off with resolution to *be* better, to *do* better, and then grown weary and given up. The elixir that revives them had come from Au Co and had been handed down from mother to daughter for generations. The masculine side of our nature – the go-getting, aggressive side which had led them thus far – is sustained and renewed by the quieter, more circumspect feminine side.

The fish Mi had rescued, rescues them. Our good deeds return to help us. She takes them some of the way, but the last part of the journey they must do alone. This we know from our own lives. No matter how much we surround ourselves by friends and relatives all the really big inner events of our lives, and all the most crucial decisions and choices, have to be made alone.

They pass through three portals. Books have been written about the significance of the number three. In every culture it is a potent and powerful symbol. It represents the soul, while four represents the body.[1] They have travelled a long way but must pass through three more purifications of the soul before they stand before the mighty deity.

They enter the hall and stand before an apparently empty throne. Hung and Mi present their petition to the throne; it is enough that it is the symbol of the godhead – they do not ask for the godhead himself. It is only when they have completed the process of prayer that they can see the deity who was there all the time. He recognizes the jade as his pledge to help when called upon. Nearly all churches and temples keep some sacred object which is an outward and visible sign of a promise the people believe their god to have made. The Dragon Emperor grants rain as requested and returns with Hung and Mi to share the celebrations of his people.

Up to this time he has been a remote and frightening presence, but Hung and Mi, by their courage and effort, have brought him to the people so that they might express their gratitude personally. The fact that Hung and Mi have to bring him the gourd of water before he can make the rain emphasizes once again that the relationship between deity and mortal has to be two-way. We have an old, true saying: 'God helps those who help themselves', and I think that is one of the important messages of the story.

That the deity is a dragon might puzzle some Western readers, because in Western tradition the dragon is more often than not depicted as some evil monster to be slain. There are many representations of St George or St Michael doing battle with such a creature. The Christian Church associated it with the pagan religion it was trying to supersede. For example, the font in the little church at Avebury in Wiltshire, England, the site of an ancient stone circle, depicts a bishop with his foot on the head of a dragon/serpent, no doubt representing the triumph of the Church over the ancient neolithic and Bronze Age religion that used the stone circle as temple. But in Eastern tradition the dragon plays a very different role. When lying beneath the earth it symbolizes the strong and sinuous power of earth energy. When hidden deep in the sea it controls the rains that sustain life on earth. It is supernatural and awe-inspiring, but it is also positive, creative, life-giving and life-enhancing. It is to be revered and used, not destroyed and wasted.

Recently, the growing interest in Eastern religion and mysticism has given Westerners the concept of 'yin and yang'. This story illustrates very well that nothing can be achieved without the perfect balance of yin and yang. Au Co, Mi and the princess represent the feminine principle, or yin, the instinctive, intuitive, guiding faculty by which we are inspired to look in the right direction for a way out of our predicament. Hung and the Dragon Emperor represent the masculine principle, or yang, the active, rational, practical faculty by which the problem is solved. If you like you can see this as the right and the left side of the brain. Note that we are talking about the feminine and the masculine *principle* here — not man and woman *as such*.

15

The Seven Voyages of Sindbad the Sailor

ARABIA

> ### Origin

THE ORIGINAL 'thousand and one' stories of the collection known to us as *The Arabian Nights* were supposed to have been told by the princess Sheherazade to the king of India and China, Shahriar, in an effort to entertain him so that he would not behead her as he had all of his other wives. In fact, the stories were no doubt collected over the centuries from India, Persia and the Arab countries. Many of them were discovered in manuscript form at the beginning of the eighteenth century by the French scholar, Antoine Galland, who made the first translation for Christian European audiences. It was believed that the voyages of Sindbad the Sailor took place when the caliph of Baghdad was Harun-al-Rashid sometime between AD 786 and 809, but whether Sindbad actually existed or whether the stories attributed to him were just a hotchpotch of sailor's yarns dating from the eighth to the eleventh centuries when Arab navigators were sailing the trade route between the Middle East and China, we do not know.

The stories of Sheherazade have been told and retold over many centuries in many countries, and there is no definitive text. The collection I grew up with was *Stories from the Arabian Nights*, based on a translation from the Arabic by Edward William Lane.

SINDBAD SETS OFF ON A VOYAGE

The Story

THERE WAS ONCE a poor porter called Sindbad who carried heavy burdens upon his head for hire. One day he was passing the house of a rich merchant and paused wistfully at the gate to listen to the sounds of merriment coming from within. He was noticed and invited in to join the group of people gathered around the merchant. He bowed to the ground, giving his name, when asked, as Sindbad the Porter. The merchant laughed for he, too, was called Sindbad – Sindbad the Sailor. The porter was invited to stay and listen to the merchant's tales of adventure and how his fortunes had fluctuated over the years.

'For poor as you are now,' he said to the porter, 'I have been poorer.'

It seemed he had been born to a merchant father and had known riches as a youth, but on his father's death had so squandered his inheritance that he found himself destitute. Selling his last remaining possessions, he embarked with other merchants on a ship.

After some time sailing they came upon an island and put ashore. There they made fires to cook their meal, but the ground suddenly moved and to their horror they found that they were not on an island at all but on the back of a huge sea creature who, feeling the heat of the fires, was preparing to plunge to the depths of the ocean. Many of the merchants were drowned but Sindbad managed to climb into a huge wooden bowl and stay afloat. After many long and desperate days he was washed up on the shore and there became employed by a rich and noble king. By chance, one day, his old ship came to harbour and at last he could return to his own country. Rich now from the gifts he had received from his royal employer, he lived the good life once more, always keeping Allah's commands in mind to give to the poor and to care for his family. At the end of the story of his first voyage he gave Sindbad the Porter a hundred gold coins and sent him on his way, telling him to return the following day for another story.

For seven days the porter came to the rich merchant's house and each day heard a different tale. At the end of each dangerous and difficult adventure it seemed the merchant returned thankfully to Baghdad, vowing never to leave home again, only to become restless and, forgetting the discomforts of his last journey, set off once more. After each story-telling he gave the porter a hundred gold coins.

On the second voyage Sindbad the Sailor set sail on a goodly merchant vessel and passed from port to port buying and selling and accumulating wealth. One day they came to a beautiful island and put in to shore to stock up with fresh water. Sindbad fell asleep under a tree; when he woke he found that the ship had sailed on without him. For a while he bemoaned his fate, but then set about exploring the island. He found no habitation or living soul, but a strange, white, spherical dome that had neither door nor window.

Suddenly the sky became dark and, looking up, he saw a gigantic bird hovering over the dome and realized that it was the creature's egg. Sindbad remained hidden until nearly dawn when he decided to tie himself to the bird's foot, hoping that it would carry him to a place within reach of civilization.

THE ROC (A MYTHICAL BIRD)

It did, in fact, lift him off the earth and carry him a long way, but where it deposited him proved to be worse than the place he had left. He was in a deep ravine with no means of climbing the steep cliffs that surrounded him. Looking around, he found the ground was rich in diamonds and other precious stones, but as night fell the place became alive with serpents. He climbed into a cave and blocked the entrance with a large boulder to keep the serpents out, but found to his terror that at the back of the cave itself a huge snake was sleeping over its eggs. He dared not sleep himself but watched all night. In the morning he emerged, exhausted and hungry.

Suddenly the carcass of a sheep fell from above. At first he was puzzled and then remembered a story he had been told by other sailors. It seemed that men, knowing there were diamonds in the valley but having no means of reaching them, devised a method for obtaining them. They threw down meat to which the diamonds adhered and then, when the great birds seized the meat and carried it up to the top of the cliffs, the men frightened them so that they dropped the meat – and the men could seize the diamonds. Sindbad filled his clothes with diamonds and tied himself to the carcass of the sheep. When the huge bird took the meat to the top of the cliff he was taken as well, and when the men frightened the bird away, they found Sindbad. Telling his story and giving them some of the diamonds, he was taken back to their city, whence he made his way back to Baghdad.

On his third journey his ship was driven off course in a storm and boarded by a host of vicious-looking apes. Some of the sailors swam ashore to escape from them. There they found a deserted house in which they wearily sought shelter. Unfortunately, it was the house of a giant by whom they were imprisoned and eaten one by one. Secretly, Sindbad had the idea to make rafts of the firewood when the giant slept and to sharpen two iron stakes, which they heated in the fire. When the giant approached again they drove the stakes into his eyes and blinded him – and thus escaped. But their troubles were not over, for the island to which they fled on the rafts was inhabited by a giant serpent who ate the sailors one by one, just as the giant had done. Sindbad alone escaped by tying a framework of logs around himself so that when the snake tried to swallow him, it could not. It was his good fortune that soon after a ship called at the island and took him away.

During his fourth voyage he was shipwrecked in a tempest but managed to float on some planks to the shore of an island. Almost immediately he and the other survivors were captured by savages who took them before their king. Starving, they fell upon the food they were offered and ate ravenously. Only Sindbad found it so revolting he could not swallow a mouthful. He watched in some alarm how stupefied his companions became as they stuffed more and more food into their mouths. Over the next few days it became clear that the savages were cannibals and were fattening the sailors up like cattle for the pot. Sindbad himself became so thin and bony they ignored him and he managed to escape.

Eventually he came to a city where he noticed the inhabitants, though living well and comfortably, rode horses without saddles. He set about making a saddle at once and, before long, he was a rich saddlemaker very much in favour with the king. He was given a beautiful wife and spent his days and nights in pleasure and luxury until one day his wife died and, as was the custom in that country, he was buried with her in a deep cave. He would have died there like many others had he not spied an animal in the cave and followed it until it led him to the hole through which it had come. He loaded himself with the jewels and riches that had been buried with the dead and made his way out of the cave. It was not long before he hailed a passing ship and was once more in Baghdad.

By the time of his fifth voyage Sindbad the Sailor was in the position to buy and outfit a great ship of his own. All went well until one day his men landed on an island and started throwing stones at a great white dome they found. He called out at once to stop them, but it was too late; the giant roc's egg was broken and the parent birds were swooping down for revenge. They tried to sail away as fast as they could, but the angry birds pursued them, dropping great boulders on the ship until it sank. Once again, Sindbad was in the water with all his possessions lost. Once again, with the help of Allah and his own ingenuity, he found a plank and was carried ashore.

He found himself among lush forests with plenty of fruit to eat and fresh water to drink. After a time he came upon an old, hairy man sitting by a stream and tried to start up a conversation. But the man would not reply, only making signs that he would like to be carried from that place. Sindbad obligingly lifted him upon his back and set off to explore the forest further. But when he was weary and wished to put his burden down the man refused to get off and clung more firmly – almost strangling the sailor. Nothing he could do would free him of the old man, whose legs, black and wrinkled, were fastened like vices around Sindbad's body. At last Sindbad thought of a way out of his predicament. He found a dried-out gourd and filled it with grapes and sealed it up. After a time the grapes fermented; he opened the gourd and pretended to drink with relish. The old man seized the gourd from him and drained its contents. When he was well and truly intoxicated, Sindbad managed to loosen his legs and free himself.

A passing ship took him from the island, but when he landed on another to refresh himself they sailed off without him. He found his way to a city, but was warned that at night the place was besieged by apes. He joined a group of men who gathered pebbles in the day to throw at the apes at night. The apes fought back by throwing coconuts. Sindbad gathered them up and, when another ship came to the city, he embarked on it and began to trade his coconuts for cinnamon and pepper and aloe-wood, even pearls, and thus, once more, amassed a fortune.

On his sixth voyage the ship he was on was driven off course by tempest once again and wrecked upon a shore rich in treasure from other wrecked ships. But food was scarce and, one by one, his companions died. Determined not to do the same, he built a raft, loaded it with treasure, and rowed it up the river that disappeared into the interior. For a while all went well and then the river disappeared into the side of a mountain. For many a long hour he was in pitch darkness, in danger of being squeezed and trapped between narrow cavern walls. At last he emerged on the other side in a country rich in jewels, with kindly people who fed him and took him to their king. There at court he lived for some time, witnessing great processions of dignitaries on elephants and various other wonders. When he became restless for his home, the king of India released him with a letter of greeting and wonderful gifts, including a ruby cup set with pearls, for Caliph Harun-al-Rashid.

Sindbad had decided that this was definitely the last voyage he would undertake, but the caliph insisted that he return to India with a letter and gifts from himself to the king. On the way Sindbad's boat was set upon by pirates and once again he found himself naked and destitute in a strange land. He was soon befriended, however, by a man who put him in a tree with a bow and arrow and asked that each night he should shoot an elephant when the herd came down to the water-hole to drink. This he did until the elephants turned on him; one seized him in its trunk and carried him away. He expected to be slain but was deposited instead among a huge heap of elephant bones and tusks and left alone. Realizing that there was an untold wealth of ivory there for the taking, without having to kill for it, Sindbad was soon an immensely rich man again.

Buying a boat, he sailed on and came to a land even stranger than any he had seen before. There, once a month, the inhabitants sprouted wings and took to the air like birds. Sindbad persuaded one man to take him up with him and experienced the rush of air, the dizzy height, the landscape unfolding like a magnificent carpet beneath him. He had been lifted into the air by the great roc – but this, this was flying free under one's own control. Surely this was the journey to end all journeys.

When Sindbad the Sailor returned to Baghdad after the seventh voyage, he, the rich merchant, took the hands of Sindbad the Porter, a poor man no longer, and they became inseparable companions for the rest of their lives.

THE LAST VOYAGE OF SINDBAD, WHERE HE COMES TO A LAND
IN WHICH THE INHABITANTS DEVELOP WINGS AND FLY LIKE BIRDS

Commentary

ONE OF THE most interesting devices for me in this series of traveller's tales is that of Sindbad the Porter, the poor man of the same name as the rich merchant, who stays throughout the recital, steadily growing richer, and ending up being the merchant's closest friend.

That they are both called Sindbad might alert us to the fact that they are two sides of the same coin — however, if they are thought of as separate people, the porter represents the steady, slow and ultimately safer approach to life, and Sindbad the Sailor the mercurial, dashing, reckless, adventurous approach that gives the greatest rewards but also the greatest suffering. The porter, the ordinary man, carries the burdens of the speculator, the adventurer. Without him the merchant cannot operate. Without him the story-teller has no audience. The sailor needs to tell his tales — the porter needs to have vicarious adventures. No wonder they become inseparable companions. Even if the porter is part of Sindbad the Sailor himself — how often do we tell ourselves the stories of our adventures, embellishing them as we go, before ever we find a willing listener outside ourselves? Sometimes the only way we can endure the disasters that occur is by remaking them into stories for ourselves and for others. We 'dine out' on our disasters in order to comfort ourselves.

The characters of both the Sindbads are worthy. One is steady, dependable, humble and cautious. The other is foolhardy, courageous, clever, quick to turn every disadvantage to an advantage. When the apes throw coconuts he thinks at once of how much he can sell them for. The porter, we feel, would have left them lying on the ground, fled, and gained nothing from the experience.

The tale of Sindbad's voyages is similar to several others in world tradition, such as the sixth-century Irish voyages of Maeldun and Brendan, and the Greek travels of Odysseus. Today we have *Star Trek* where, each week, we are told of a fresh adventure in a different area of space. The driving force is the restlessness of man — the same restlessness that drove Vasco da Gama around the Cape of Good Hope, Magellan around the Horn, Columbus to America and Neil Armstrong to the Moon. May it never cease!

In 1980 Tim Severin mounted an expedition sponsored by the Ministry of National Heritage and Culture in Oman to prove that Sindbad's voyages *could* have taken place. He drew his information from early records of Arab seafaring, built a ship of the type that would have been used by Sindbad and his contemporaries, and sailed it successfully the 6000 miles (9600 km) to China. The fabulous gemstones of Sri Lanka, the elephants of India, the cannibals and orang-utans of Sumatra . . . the cinnamon and pearls and aloes . . . the coconuts and pepper . . . are all easily placed *en route*. The frequent shipwrecks and tempests that blew him off course are equally understandable given the climate of the region and the flimsiness of the early sailing ships.

These stories would not still entertain us in the twentieth century without other and deeper levels. We know men such as Sindbad the Sailor and Sindbad the Porter today, and we know that what happens to them is happening even now on a symbolic level to us. The 'old man' that clings to Sindbad's back and nearly throttles him may be an orang-utan, but

CHERYL YAMBRACH ROSE ©

it may also be the suffocating burden of old attitudes and prejudices that prevent us going forward. The raw meat Sindbad has to tie on to himself to get out of the chasm may be a genuine trick used by miners to obtain diamonds, but it may also represent the raw and therefore unpalatable truths we have to accept before we can achieve spiritual riches, the chasm out of which we can only come with the help of the winged spirit.

Sometimes misfortunes come upon Sindbad through no fault of his own – tempests, for example, sink his ship. But at other times his own carelessness brings misfortune upon him. He falls asleep and is left behind. On a journey, any journey, one's wits must be continually awake and sharp. In every case he gets out of trouble by his own ingenuity and his touching faith in Allah, and this is what makes us love and admire him. That he goes back to base and determines never to wander again, only to find in the end that he cannot live without the spice of adventure, touches our hearts. He is the man of action we admire in a hundred action movies, the hero who wins through against every adversity while we sit in our armchairs and watch from a safe distance like Sindbad the Porter, wishing we could be like him – believing that we could – but too afraid to try and be proved wrong.

The serpent sleeping over its eggs in the cavern, and the giant serpent that swallows his shipmates, but not him, because he rigs up a contraption of logs around him, may represent – as serpents usually do in legend and myth – the deep, dark, dangerous stirring of the subconscious which, in the one case, he acknowledges but does not disturb and, in the other, does battle with and defeats. The apes that attack the ship and again have to be driven off at night by the throwing of pebbles are, in one sense, genuine apes common in the Far East and, in another, the ever-present mischievous trickster in the psyche, always trying to make one break the rules, defy authority, bring about chaos and anarchy. The sea creature whose gigantic back the sailors mistook for an island might well represent the 'false start' to the journey of the soul, when we are putting our trust in illusory and ephemeral things.

The giant who has to be blinded in order for the hero to escape is a common theme in these kinds of stories throughout the world. We have to stop seeing with the eyes of our old self, the self that holds us back and threatens to devour all our highest inclinations . . .

The giant roc is reminiscent of the condor in present-day South America. Is this some giant bird once common in the East that is now extinct? Or is it a symbol for Sindbad's first clumsy attempts to get off the earth into the rarer atmosphere of spiritual exploration later achieved in China? (There is a persistent legend that the ancient Chinese had kites which could take the weight of a man and frequently used them for flight. In the light of Chinese ingenuity and the fact that hang-gliders are a relatively simple construction, this may well have had some truth in it!)

In the first instance the roc helps Sindbad because its egg has not been harmed. In the second instance he tries to stop his thoughtless shipmates destroying the egg but cannot, and his ship is destroyed by the bird. Smaller birds have been known to drop stones on tortoises in order to get at the meat, so it is well within imaginative bounds that a giant bird will drop a boulder on a ship that threatens its young.

Symbolically, the bird represents the spirit capable of soaring to great heights. The sailors destroyed the egg because of the earthbound limitations of their vision. The bird destroys the voyagers' ship (but not the true voyager) with a piece of the same earth they are incapable of seeing beyond.

If this series of voyages is to be read as yet another sequence in the progress of the soul towards spiritual attainment we must note that Sindbad starts travelling from an inner restlessness, passes through many illuminating vicissitudes, attempts to take off from the limitations of being earthbound twice with the help of the giant bird, and finally achieves true flight in China (the land stranger than any other he had encountered), after which he is no longer restless. We may note that the seventh journey was not his own idea; he was obeying a higher authority. It is on this journey that he is given a gift by the elephants (Nature) and learns to be rich without killing and exploitation. It is on this journey that he learns that human beings are capable of flight both literally and spiritually.

16

The Quest for the White Bird

SOUTHERN (AFRICA)

Origin

I FOUND THIS story many years ago in a book by Laurens van der Post called *The Heart of the Hunter*[1] and it has haunted me ever since. It is very simple and very profound, and makes a perfect finale to this book about sacred, mythic and legendary journeys. Laurens van der Post heard it when he was a boy from an elderly Hottentot shepherd in South Africa.

In the early 1930s, when I was a child in Pretoria, South Africa, a neighbour had a servant who, I was told, was a Hottentot. He was an old, old man who used to sit sometimes on the back steps of their kitchen verandah (or 'stoep' as we called it) and tell me stories. I remember asking him what a 'Hottentot' was and his face of a thousand wrinkles seemed to sink in on itself with sadness. The Khoikhoin peoples, called by their European conquerors 'the Hottentots', and the San peoples, called 'Bushmen', were the primary races of South Africa, slaughtered and ousted by both the Bantus invading from the north and the Europeans invading from the sea. The remnants of both races are now mostly to be found in Namibia or the Kalahari. I wish I had written down all those meaningful stories he told me, but, as a child, I had no idea what a precious gift I was being given.

But perhaps the gift was not wasted after all. Nothing ever is. Perhaps my abiding interest in stories that have significant and hidden levels of meaning comes from that illiterate story-teller, and not from reading books by Jung and Joseph Campbell as an adult.

KHOIKHOIN WARRIOR IN TRAVELLING CLOTHES

KHOIKHOIN WARRIOR IN TRADITIONAL COSTUME

CHERYL YAMBRACH ROSE

The Story

A HUNTER CAME to a pool to fill a gourd with water. As he bent down he saw the reflection of a white bird behind his own face on the still, silvered surface. He was astonished at its beauty and its size and looked up at once, thinking that he would indeed be honoured if he could return to his people with such a bird. A chief would be proud to wear its feathers.

But the bird had already flown away over the tall, dark trees of the forest, and was out of sight.

He set off in pursuit, leaving his family, his friends and his tribe, nothing diverting him from his determination to find the bird.

He never caught another glimpse of it – but wherever he went he heard news of its passing.

He came at last to a great mountain with snow on its top. The people in the region thought they had seen the bird on the summit.

He began to climb, but found that his progress was becoming slower and slower. His limbs ached. His breath came with difficulty. He had not noticed it, but in the long years of search he had been growing older. Now, an old man, he could barely climb to the top of the mountain.

Finally he reached the summit and lay there in despair. His life had passed and it seemed to him he had achieved nothing.

'Oh, Mother!' he cried. And again: 'Oh, Mother!'

A voice seemed to answer him. 'Look up,' it said. 'Look up!'

And he looked up.

Spiralling through the air towards him was a single shining white feather. With tears in his eyes he reached up and grasped it.

With the feather in his hand, and a smile of contentment on his face, the hunter died.

Commentary

'WHAT SORT OF bird was it, old father?' Laurens van der Post asked the Hottentot shepherd.

'No one knows its name,' the old man replied.

No one knows its name.

But the goddess of wisdom and truth and of cosmic order and harmony in ancient Egypt was called 'Ma'at' – and on her head she wore a single feather. When someone died and passed into the Otherworld their hearts were weighed against the feather of truth in the scales of Osiris, Lord of Death and Resurrection.

THE WHITE FEATHER OF THE SACRED BIRD

Notes

Preface

1   The Venerable Bede, translated by Leo Sherley-Price, *A History of the English Church and People*, 1955, Book II, chapter 13.

1   Gilgamesh: The Quest for Immortality

1   Robert Temple, *He Who Saw Everything*, 1991, Tablet VI, p. 67.
2   Ibid., Tablet VIII, p. 81.
3   Ibid., Tablet X, p. 115.
4   Ibid., Tablet XI, p. 124.
5   S. H. Hooke, *The Penguin Middle Eastern Mythology*, 1985. p. 54 (quoted from J. B. Pritchard, *The Ancient Near Eastern Texts relating to the Old Testament*, p. 90).
6   Austen H. Layard, *Discoveries in the Ruins of Nineveh and Babylon*, 1853, p. 294.

2   Jason and the Quest for the Golden Fleece

1   1.6-hectare.
2   Genesis 22.13.
3   Mark 9.37.

3   The Journey of the Rainbow Snake

1   James G. Cowan, *The Elements of the Aborigine Tradition*, 1992, pp. 32–4.
2   Wally Caruana, *Aboriginal Art*, 1993, p. 164.
3   Ibid., pp. 162, 163.
4   A. W. Reed, *Aboriginal Myths*, 1992, p. 79.
5   Joseph Campbell, *Historical Atlas of World Mythology*, 1988, vol. I, part 2, p. 140.
6   Ibid., p. 141.
7   James G. Cowan, op. cit., p. 36.
8   Yves Bonnefoy, *Mythologies (American, African and Old European)*, 1993, p. 148.
9   Sheila Savill, *Pears Encyclopaedia of Myths and Legends: Western and Northern Europe, Central and Southern Africa*, 1977, pp. 153–4.

4   The Journey of Merytamun to the Hall of Osiris

1   R. O. Faulkner (trans.), *The Ancient Egyptian Book of the Dead*, 1985, spells 110, 125, 144, 146 and 149.
2   Evelyn Rossiter, *The Book of the Dead: Famous Egyptian Papyri*, 1984, p. 110.
3   Alan W. Shorter, *The Egyptian Gods: A Handbook*, 1979, pp. 53, 55, 56, 66, 68.
4   A cubit is an ancient measure of length, approximately equal to the length of the forearm.
5   Emmer is a species of wheat.
6   An atef crown was associated with universal power and dominion. See Evelyn Rossiter, op. cit., p. 21.
7   The uas-sceptre, in imitation of a shepherd's crook, signified power, dominion and protection.
8   Uraei were sacred serpents.

5   Kivanga's Journey to the Underworld to Bring Back His Twin

1   Yves Bonnefoy, *Mythologies (American, African and Old European)* , 1993, p. 152.
2   Ibid., p. 118.
3   John 1.1.
4   Yves Bonnefoy, op. cit., p. 158.

9   The Shaman's Celestial Journey

1   Mircea Eliade, *Shamanism: Archaic Techniques of Ecstasy*, 1974, pp. 127–31.

12   The Three Journeys of Ilya of Murom

1   Genesis 18.

13   The Voyage of Maeldun

1   T. W. Rolleston, *Myths and Legends of the Celtic Race*, 1911, p. 312.
2   Ibid., p. 315.
3   Ibid., p. 316.
4   Ibid., p. 316.
5   Ibid., p. 316.
6   Ibid., p. 317.
7   Ibid., p. 320.
8   Ibid., p. 321.
9   Ibid., p. 325.
10   J. C. Cooper, *An Illustrated Encyclopaedia of Traditional Symbols*, 1978, p. 119.
11   T. W. Rolleston, op. cit., p. 314.
12   J. C. Cooper, op. cit., p. 188.
13   Ibid., p. 193.
14   Ibid., p. 105.
15   T. W. Rolleston, op. cit., p. 322.
16   Tim Severin, *The Brendan Voyage*, 1979, p. 111.
17   Ibid., p. 159.
18   Ibid., p. 207.

14   The Journey to the Dragon Emperor's Palace

1   For an excellent analysis of the number three, see J. C. Cooper, *An Illustrated Encyclopaedia of Traditional Symbols*, pp. 114, 115.

16   The Quest for the White Bird

1   Laurens van der Post, *The Heart of the Hunter*, 1968, p. 167.

Bibliography

Preface

The Venerable Bede, *A History of the English Church and People*, translated by Leo Sherley-Price, Penguin Books, Harmondsworth, 1955.

1 Gilgamesh: The Quest for Immortality

Hooke, S. H., *Middle Eastern Mythology*, Penguin Books, Harmondsworth, 1985.

Layard, Austen H., *Discoveries in the Ruins of Nineveh and Babylon*, John Murray, London, 1853.

Sanders, N. K., *The Epic of Gilgamesh*, Penguin Books, Harmondsworth, 1960.

Temple, Robert, *He Who Saw Everything: A Verse Translation of 'The Epic of Gilgamesh'*, Rider, London, 1991.

2 Jason and the Quest for the Golden Fleece

Brown, Janet, *The Voyage of the Argonauts*, Methuen, London, 1925.

Bulfinch, Thomas, *The Golden Age of Myth and Legend*, George Harrap and Co., London, 1917.

Graves, Robert, *The Greek Myths*, Penguin Books, Harmondsworth, 1955.

Hope Moncrieff, A. R., *Classic Myth and Legend*, Senate, London, 1993.

Jacobs, Joseph, *The Book of Wonder Voyages*, David Nutt, London, 1896.

Larousse Encyclopaedia of Mythology, translated by Richard Aldington and Delano Ames, Hamlyn, London, 1959.

Rieu, E. V., *The Voyage of the Argo*, Penguin Books, Harmondsworth, 1959.

Severin, Tim, *The Jason Voyage*, Hutchinson, London, 1985.

3 The Journey of the Rainbow Snake

Bonnefoy, Yves, *Mythologies (American, African and Old European)*, translated under the direction of Wendy Doniger, University of Chicago Press, London, 1993.

Campbell, Joseph, *Historical Atlas of World Mythology*, vol. I, part 2, Harper and Row, New York, 1988.

Caruana, Wally, *Aboriginal Art*, Thames and Hudson, London, 1993.

Cowan, James G., *The Elements of the Aborigine Tradition*, Element Books, Shaftesbury, 1992.

——, *Kur-man-gur the Rainbow Serpent*, Barefoot Books, London, 1994.

Edwards, Robert and Bruce Guerin, *Aboriginal Bark Painting*, Rigby, Melbourne, 1974.

Reed, A. W., *Aboriginal Myths: Tales of the Dreamtime*, Reed Books, West Chatswood, NSW, 1992.

Savill, Sheila, *Pears Encyclopaedia of Myths and Legends: Western and Northern Europe, Central and Southern Africa*, Pelham Books and Book Club Associates, London, 1977.

4 The Journey of Merytamun to the Hall of Osiris

Baines, John and Jaromír Málek, *Atlas of Ancient Egypt*, Phaidon, Oxford, 1980.

Cooper, J. C., *An Illustrated Encyclopaedia of Traditional Symbols*, Thames and Hudson, London, 1978.

Ellis, Normandi, *Awakening Osiris: A New Translation of 'The Egyptian Book of the Dead'*, Phanes Press, Grand Rapids, Michigan, 1988.

Faulkner, R. O. (trans.), *The Ancient Egyptian Book of the Dead*, British Museum Publications, London, 1985.

Hart, George, *A Dictionary of Egyptian Gods and Goddesses*, Routledge and Kegan Paul, London, 1986.

Lurker, Manfred, *The Gods and Symbols of Ancient Egypt*, translated by Barbara Cummings, Thames and Hudson, London, 1980.

Rossiter, Evelyn, *The Book of the Dead: Famous Egyptian Papyri*, Liber SA and Editions Minerva, Geneva, 1984.

Rundle Clark, R. T., *Myth and Symbol in Ancient Egypt*, Thames and Hudson, London, 1978.

Shorter, Alan W., *The Egyptian Gods: A Handbook*, Routledge and Kegan Paul, London, 1979.

Wallis Budge, E. A., *Egyptian Religion: Egyptian Ideas of the Future Life*, Routledge and Kegan Paul, London, 1979.

—— (trans.), *The Book of the Dead*, Routledge and Kegan Paul, London, 1949.

5 Kivanga's Journey to the Underworld to Bring Back his Twin

Bonnefoy, Yves, *Mythologies (American, African and Old European)*, translated under the direction of Wendy Doniger, University of Chicago Press, London, 1993.

6 The Quest for the Holy Grail

Eschenbach, Wolfram von, *Parzival*, translated by Helen M. Mustard and Charles E. Passage, Vintage Books, New York, 1961; another translation is by A. T. Hatto, Penguin Books, Harmondsworth, 1980.

Fife, Graeme, *Arthur the King: The Themes behind the Legends*, BBC Books, London, 1990.

Gantz, Jeffrey (trans.), *The Mabinogion*, Penguin Books, Harmondsworth, 1976.

Guerber, H. A., *Middle Ages: Myths and Legends*, Senate, London, 1994.

Guest, Lady Charlotte (trans.), *The Mabinogion*, J. M. Dent, Everyman's Library, London, 1906.

Jung, Emma and Marie-Louise von Franz, *The Grail Legend*, translated by Andrea Dykes, Sigo Press, Boston; Coventure, London, 1986.

Matarasso, P. M. (trans.), *The Quest for the Holy Grail*, Penguin Books, Harmondsworth, 1969.
Original author unknown; scholars claim it was first written *c.* 1225, some say by Walter Map, who died in 1209.

Matthews, John (ed.), *At the Table of the Grail*, Routledge and Kegan Paul, London, 1984.

——, *King Arthur and the Grail Quest: Myth and Vision from Celtic Times to the Present*, Blandford, London, 1994.

——, *The Grail: The Quest for the Eternal*, Thames and Hudson, London, 1981.

——, and Marian Green, *The Grail Seeker's Companion: A Grail Guide to the Grail Quest in the Aquarian Age*, The Aquarian Press, Wellingborough, 1986.

7 The Death of Baldur

Anson, W. S. W. (ed.), *Asgard of the Gods: Tales and Traditions of our Northern Ancestors*, adapted from the work of Dr W. Wagner by M. W. Macdowall; Swan Sonnenschein, Le Bas and Lowrey, London, 1886.

Bulfinch, Thomas, *The Golden Age of Myth and Legend*, George Harrap and Co., London, 1917.

Ellis Davidson, H. R., *Scandinavian Mythology* (in the series 'Library of the World's Myths and Legends'), Hamlyn, London, 1982.

Guerber, H. A., *The Norsemen: Myths and Legends*, Senate, London, 1994.

8 The Journey of Nala and Damayanti

Mackenzie, Donald A., *Myths and Legends of India*, Senate, London, 1994. See pp. 328–73.

——, *The World's Heritage*, The Gresham Publishing Co., London, 1918.

The Sister Nivedita (Margaret E. Noble) of Ramakrishna–Vivekanada and Ananda K. Coomaraswamy, *Myths of the Hindus and Buddhists*, George Harrap and Co., London, 1913. See pp. 356–67.

9 The Shaman's Celestial Journey

Eliade, Mircea, *Shamanism: Archaic Techniques of Ecstasy*, Princeton University Press, 1974.

10 The Journey of Bran's Head

Gantz, Jeffrey (trans.), *The Mabinogion*, Penguin Books, Harmondsworth, 1976.

Guest, Lady Charlotte (trans.), *The Mabinogion*, J. M. Dent, Everyman's Library, London, 1906.

11 The Journey to the Fourth World

Leeming, David Adams, *The World of Myth*, Oxford University Press, 1990.

Waters, Frank and Oswald White Bear Fredericks, *The Book of the Hopi: The First Revelation of the Hopi's Historical and Religious World View of Life*, Penguin Books, Harmondsworth, 1977.

12 The Three Journeys of Ilya of Murom

Armstrong, David, *Russian Lacquer Boxes*, Forkis Publishers, Moscow, 1992.

Downing, Charles, *Russian Tales and Legends*, Oxford University Press, 1993.

13 The Voyage of Maeldun

Cooper, J. C., *An Illustrated Encyclopaedia of Traditional Symbols*, Thames and Hudson, London, 1978.

Guest, Lady Charlotte (trans.), *The Mabinogion*, J. M. Dent, Everyman's Library, London, 1906.

Jacobs, Joseph, *The Book of Wonder Voyages*, David Nutt, London, 1896.

Matthews, Caitlín, *The Celtic Book of the Dead*, St Martin's Press, New York, 1992.

Rolleston, T. W., *Myths and Legends of the Celtic Race*, George Harrap and Co., London, 1911.

Severin, Tim, *The Brendan Voyage*, Arrow Books, 1979.

14 The Journey to the Dragon Emperor's Palace

Cooper, J. C., *An Illustrated Encyclopaedia of Traditional Symbols*, Thames and Hudson, London, 1978.

Cotterell, Arthur, *Illustrated Encyclopaedia of Myths and Legends*, Cassell, London, 1992.

Thich Nhat Hanh, *A Taste of Earth and Other Legends of Vietnam*, translated by Mobi Warren, Parallax Press, Berkeley, California, 1993.

15 The Seven Voyages of Sindbad the Sailor

Lane, Edward William (trans.), *Stories from the Arabian Nights*, selected, edited and arranged for young people by Frances Jenkins Olcott; George Harrap and Co., London, 1913.

Severin, Tim, *The Sindbad Voyage*, Hutchinson, London, 1982.

16 The Quest for the White Bird

Post, Laurens van der, *The Heart of the Hunter*, Penguin Books, Harmondsworth, 1965.

Index